CYTOCHEMISTRY
A Critical Approach

A VOLUME IN THE WILEY
BIOLOGICAL RESEARCH SERIES

This Series includes a number of small volumes covering various topics in biology. The purpose is to provide other scientists with an authoritative orientation in the author's work as quickly as possible. To provide this orientation, each author will be asked to stress his own work and his own viewpoints without loss of proper perspective of the field as a whole.

Previously Published

CYTOCHEMISTRY

A Critical Approach

J. F. DANIELLI

Professor of Zoology
King's College
London, W.C. 2

JOHN WILEY & SONS, INC., NEW YORK
CHAPMAN & HALL, LIMITED, LONDON

Library of Congress Catalog Card Number: 52-12420

To the Memory of
Sir Jack Drummond

ACKNOWLEDGMENTS

This book contains a slightly enlarged version of the material presented in a series of lectures given in the Department of Zoology of the University of Chicago, in the spring of 1949, during the tenure of a Rockefeller Fellowship. The main work of preparing the manuscript was carried out at the Marine Biological Laboratory, Woods Hole, during the tenure of a Lalor Fellowship.

It is a great pleasure to me to acknowledge my debt to Professor Paul Weiss, who invited me to Chicago; to Professor W. L. Doyle, who made the arrangements for my lectures; to Professor P. B. Armstrong and his colleagues, who provided such excellent facilities at Woods Hole. To the award of Rockefeller and Lalor Fellowships I largely owe this opportunity to crystallise the work on cytochemistry which has increasingly occupied my attention since 1942. A number of immediate colleagues have worked together as a team, of whom I am particularly indebted to Dr. I. J. Lorch and Dr. L. G. Bell. From numerous other friends I have benefited by help and advice, including particularly Dr. Honor B. Fell, Dr. E. Kodicek, Professor D. Keilin, Dr. H. Holter, Professor T. Caspersson, Professor B. Commoner, Dr. A. E. Mirsky, and Dr. H. Jacoby. Facilities for carrying out the researches reported here were provided by Professor J. Gray at Cambridge, by Dr. F. S. Russell at the Marine Biological Laboratory, Plymouth, and by Professor A. Haddow at the Chester Beatty Research Institute, London. During the past three years spent at King's College my group has benefited by grants from the Nuffield Foundation, the British Empire Cancer Campaign, and the Rockefeller Foundation.

CONTENTS

CHAPTER I

INTRODUCTION

Cytochemistry is an almost undeveloped branch of biology. It is only comparatively recently that a vigorous attempt has been made to solve the problems which are involved in cytochemical studies. Consequently, anything in the nature of a textbook on cytochemistry is premature. There is an insufficient body of agreed facts for it to be possible to write a textbook which would set forth a body of methods and knowledge which would be agreed to without question by the great majority of workers in this field. I wish therefore to make it clear that this book is not intended in any way as a textbook. It is very largely a record of experiments which I have carried out myself, or which have been carried out by other research workers with whom I have been closely associated. Any of the individual methods given here may well be superseded in a few years. I do, however, hope that a good deal of what is recorded here may be regarded as in the nature of a blueprint for future developments in cytochemistry. The general endeavour which is contained in this work, namely, the development of rigorous methods, is a key matter without which cytochemistry is a futile study.

Cytochemistry is pre-eminently a field which calls for a team of workers. The reason for this is that it demands a high standard of knowledge in each of the fields of biology, chemistry, and physics. Unfortunately, many of the methods which have been developed so far appear at first glance to be so simple that the necessity for rigorous treatment has largely tended to be ignored. There have, of course, been a number of outstanding instances of compliance with the experimental criteria which are required: this is obvious to all who know of the work of Feulgen, of Caspersson, or of Commoner. But the general tendency has been to suppose that anyone who can cut a tissue section and make up a standard solution is competent to carry out cytochemical investigations. Nothing could be further from the truth. Indeed,

1

it may almost be said that a good training in histology is one of the worst backgrounds possible for cytochemical work. In the type of histology and cytology which is based on showing optimal fixation, optimal staining, and optimal methods of treatment with stains, a tremendous amount depends upon the judgment of the investigator as to what he wishes to stain and just how he wishes to see it. In some sense, this type of histology and cytology is an art. On the other hand, the object of the cytochemist is to use fixatives and cytochemical methods in such a way that a specific and exact treatment is applied to a tissue, in a manner which is predetermined by the physical properties of the specimen and a precise programme of chemical treatment. During the carrying out of this programme, the judgment of the investigator must be suspended in the interest of maintaining the precision of treatment. It is only after the full processes of physical and chemical treatment have been carried through that the investigator can allow his opinion to operate. I feel obliged to add that the standards of cleanliness of reagents which are frequently adequate for classical histology are, in my experience, frequently inadequate for cytochemical purposes. So much is this so that, whenever I hear that an investigator has failed to obtain success with a cytochemical method, my first piece of advice is always that he should throw away every reagent that he has been using and make up a new set of reagents; it is surprising how frequently this elementary step is successful.

In the second half of the nineteenth century there was a considerable wave of interest in cytology and histology; this was enabled to come to fruition by the discovery of synthetic dyes which could be used for staining fixed material. It is quite clear from the literature of this period that the investigators were equally concerned to obtain information about both the physiological and the chemical organisation of protoplasm. Their success, however, was very largely limited to the morphological and physiological side: there was an almost complete failure on the chemical level. Amongst the reasons for this was the fact that affinity for a given stain is only to a limited degree determined by the detailed chemical constitution of the material being stained. It is much more markedly determined by the physical properties of the material. Difficulties were also encountered with artefacts due to fixation. This matter was brought to a head by W. B. Hardy and A. Fischer in two publications in 1899. These two investigators had a much clearer understanding of the physical basis of cytological techniques than had most of the previous workers in this field. They showed that the details of the procedure of fixation, of the nature of the fixative, and the technique of staining, have just as profound an effect upon the final picture as has the initial chemical composition of the material being stained. They also showed that many of the fixatives in common use were giving rise to structures which, in fact, did not occur in the living cells, but were precipitation artefacts. At this time, neither the chemistry nor the physics of the systems involved in cytology were sufficiently understood for it to be possible to cope with the problems demonstrated by Hardy and Fischer. Consequently, by 1910 the wave of interest in the study of fixed preparations had very largely lost its momentum so far as pioneering investigations were concerned. The pioneering investigators instead turned to working on living cells almost exclusively. There was, in consequence, a very rapid development of experimental cytology.

Between 1910 and 1935 remarkable progress was made in the field of experimental cytology. Some phenomena were so successfully analyzed that the chief physico-chemical factors involved could be detailed, and given an approximate mathematical treatment. However, the result of this successful investigation was that many of the working hypotheses formulated by the experimental cytologists postulated specific cytochemical organisations in particular parts of cells. Such postulates were found in many widely diverse fields, e.g., ciliary and amoeboid movement, muscular contraction, secretion, and the action of genes. The postulated cytochemical organisations lay so fundamentally at the heart of the mechanisms proposed that further progress was bound to become increasingly limited in every field, unless further advances were possible in cytochemistry. It is not surprising, therefore, to find that from 1935 onwards there was a renewed wave of interest in cytochemistry. Landmarks in this new wave of interest were the publication of Lison's book "Histochimie Animale," and the papers of Feulgen, Caspersson, Gomori and Takamatsu, Linderstrøm-Lang, and

Holter, who blazed new trails into the wilderness of cellular chemistry. It has, however, been somewhat unfortunate that many of the lessons which can be learned from the work of Hardy and Fischer and others have been overlooked in more recent studies.

In the development of rigorous methods of investigation in cytochemistry, it is necessary to look at each problem from three points of view: as a chemist, as a physicist, and as a biologist. From the point of view of the physicist, the main problems arise from diffusion and adsorption artefacts, from estimating errors which may arise from the state of aggregation of the substance which is being studied, from the degree of molecular orientation of the substance, and from the scattering of light within a specimen. No qualitative study can be regarded as satisfactory which does not involve the elimination of diffusion and adsorption artefacts. Correspondingly, no quantitative study can be regarded as satisfactory unless the degree of aggregation of molecules in the specimen, the orientation of the molecules in the specimen, and the scattering of light within the specimen are properly taken into consideration.

From the chemist's point of view the main problems are to use methods which are of sufficient specificity and which shall be quantitative and accurate to a known extent. A further practical problem which frequently arises is to find methods which will be to a sufficient degree inert, i.e., which do not damage the specimen. The problem of chemical specificity is a particularly difficult one. The reason for this is that chemical reactions are not carried out by molecules as a whole. They are usually carried out by a very small number of atoms in a molecule. They are often affected to a marked degree by a rather larger number of neighbouring atoms; but the greater part of the molecule may well have no effect on whether a particular reaction occurs or not. Thus the specificity of a chemical reaction is limited to supplying information as to whether a particular chemical group is present in a particular part of a cell. Information as to the nature of some of the other neighbouring groups in the same molecule may sometimes be obtained by studying the rate at which a chemical reaction proceeds. But it is impossible to identify the whole of any molecules, other than the simplest, by carrying out chemical reactions. Thus, in the well-known Feulgen reaction which is commonly said to give localization of deoxyribonucleic acid, we have in fact a method which probably indicates a linkage between deoxy sugar and any other group which one can split off from the glycoside linkage at roughly the same rate as are the purines. Thus the Feulgen reaction, in fact, gives us information which is limited to telling us that deoxy sugar is present in the specimen and that it is in glycosidic linkage with a substance which can be split away by acid hydrolysis at the same rate as are certain purines. The Feulgen reaction does not tell us whether the substance which is split off is a purine, nor does it tell us whether the sugar is linked through phosphate bonds to other similar units so as to complete a nucleic acid. In a similar way, when the ultraviolet spectrum of a specimen is studied, one can readily detect the presence of a substance absorbing in the same region of the spectrum as the purines and pyrimidines. There are, of course, other substances which absorb in this region. A notable example, recently reported by Chayen (1952), is ascorbic acid. Thus, in a material in which ascorbic acid may occur, it is necessary to take steps to differentiate between ascorbic acid and purine groups. When all the necessary elimination of this type has been done, we can perhaps be certain that in a particular part of a specimen there is purine or pyrimidine. But it has not so far proved possible from spectro-photometric studies to determine whether the purine or pyrimidine is present as part of a nucleic acid molecule, or whether it is present in some other form, e.g., linked directly to a protein. It is notable in this connection that Panijel has recently found a protein in *Ascaris* sperm which has the same absorption spectrum as nucleic acid, containing a considerable proportion of purine, but no phosphorus.

The problems which arise from the biologist's point of view are somewhat different in nature and are less readily defined. They must, however, involve a constant awareness of the fact that an animal, and a cell, cannot be dissociated from its environment. Due respect must be paid to such principles as those of homology and analogy, and at the same time it is necessary to maintain a more rigid guard against the acceptance of generalisations than is usually necessary in the fields of physics and chemistry, owing to the fact that variables on the purely biological side are far more easily underestimated than otherwise. As examples of some of the problems which affect one from the biological point of view, may be mentioned fixation and diet. It is doubtful whether any method of fixation other than freeze-drying is really adequate for cytochemical purposes. Then, as far as diet is concerned, it will be a source of amazement to future generations to discover in how few of the papers on cytochemistry the diet of the animals used is at all defined. Yet the cytochemical pattern in organs such as the liver and intestine is astonishingly dependent upon diet. As another example, may be mentioned the work of Dr. H. Mugard (1953), who has recently shown that the cytoplasm of the ciliate *Ophryoglena atra* which has not recently fed is apparently free from the enzyme alkaline phosphatase: yet within a few seconds of the formation of a food vacuole a high concentration of phosphatase is present in the cytoplasm. For particular studies it will no doubt be equally important to define the age of the animal under investigation, the time of taking the specimen, the state of hormone activity, and other biological variables, before a generalisation on the cytochemical level may safely be embarked upon.

Before passing on to consider the fields in which I have played some part in developing techniques, a number of techniques will be considered critically, since by so doing it is possible to see many of the major hazards which exist in the field of cytochemistry, and which it has been my endeavour to avoid.

CENTRIFUGAL STRATIFICATION, ETC.

In these techniques the common principle is, by centrifugation or other methods, to separate parts of cells which differ from one another in their physical characteristics. The most usual approach is to stratify a cell by centrifugation, to separate the strata, and then examine the distribution of various substances in the different strata. In the hands of Holter and of Shapiro, this work has provided valuable information about the distribution of certain substances, particularly enzymes, in large cells such as amoebae and echinoderm eggs. There are, however, some very marked limitations to techniques of this type. Their use is usually limited to large individual cells:

cells in tissues cannot be studied readily.   Then the methods of
manipulation are not devoid of action upon cell fractions which
are under study.   For example, Shapiro found that when sea
urchin eggs are centrifuged, first so as to cause stratification
and then so as to cause the cell to divide into two halves—one
light and one heavy—the respiration of the two fragments so
formed is greater than that of the initial intact egg.   It therefore follows that in an experiment of this type either there has
been a change in the physico-chemical organisation of the
enzyme systems of the cell, or else there has been synthetic activity on the part of the cell, resulting in the formation of more
respiratory enzymes.   Whichever of these changes may have
taken place, it is clear that the final condition, as revealed by
the cell fragments, cannot be taken as a close guide to what
was happening in the intact egg.   In this connection, Holter remarks, "The only conclusions to be drawn from such experiments are those based on the distributions of *substances,* $\cdots$
[which] $\cdots$ permit, of course, only indirect conclusions with
regard to physiological activity."   In any experiments involving the destruction of the known relationships between cellular
entities, as is the case in stratification, any deduction is dubious
unless it is established that the procedure does not lead to synthesis or to destruction of chemical components.   It is obligatory
in such experiments to establish the lack of such synthesis or
degradation.

MACERATION PROCEDURES

Amongst the most common techniques employed today, particularly by biochemists seeking to make a contribution to
cytology, are techniques involving the disintegration of cells
into fragments, and fractionation of the fragments so formed.
The debris formed by maceration is commonly centrifuged at
various speeds so as to isolate fragments with different sedi-
mentation rates.   It is hoped that methods of this type will
isolate granules, mitochondria, nuclei, and chromosomes, in a
condition which is closely similar to, if not identical with, the
state of those bodies in the intact cells.   It would undoubtedly
be of the greatest value if it were true that cell organs could
be isolated in this way.   But so far there has been an almost

complete lack of proof that the bodies isolated are in the same condition as in the intact cells.

It would, indeed, be very surprising if there were not many and dramatic changes in the organisation and composition of both nuclear and cytoplasmic bodies as the result of maceration and addition of the various solutions which are used in fractionation. The nucleus and the cytoplasm are both very complex colloidal systems. Studies by Chambers and others on cell nuclei have shown that when the nucleus is removed from the cell by microdissection it commonly either sets into a gel or dissolves: in either case a profound change occurs as soon as the nucleus is removed from its normal environment. De Fonbrune, and Lorch and Danielli have found that, although a nucleus may readily be transferred from one cell to another in a viable condition provided that it does not come into contact with the environment of the cell, a few seconds' contact with the environment is sufficient to destroy the viability of the nucleus. Dr. Dounce has informed me that he has compared the composition of nuclei isolated from macerated cells by centrifugation in non-aqueous solvents with nuclei isolated by centrifugation in aqueous solvents. The nuclei from the non-aqueous solvents contain almost twice as much material as do those from the aqueous solvents. From these few remarks it is quite clear that one should anticipate profound changes in the organisation of the nucleus when it is removed from its normal environment, and that these changes must include diffusion of substances out of the nucleus, and probably also diffusion of substances into the nucleus. It should be the first responsibility of the investigator to ascertain the extent to which morphological changes and diffusion artefacts are involved in these isolation techniques. It seems probable that at the present time the only work of this type, i.e., on isolated nuclei, which is reliable is that of Brachet and of Callan on some of the properties of the whole nuclei of amphibian oocytes, which were isolated by microdissection techniques.

It is probable that the organisation of the cytoplasmic components is just as labile as that of the nucleus, if not more so. Often in relatively simple protein systems, such as blood plasma, addition of foreign materials causes profound reorganisation. For example, addition of salts may vary the proportion of albumin and globulin found on electrophoresis of plasma. Somewhat similar effects are found on simply adding water to plasma, and a not immoderate addition of water causes precipitation of part of the globulin. It is difficult to see how experiments on the isolation of granules and other small cell organs can be taken at their face value unless it is rigorously demonstrated that their composition is unchanged by the isolation procedure.

Often, if the composition of individual granules is identical or closely similar to the granules in the living cells, there still remain many difficulties in interpretation of experiments on the mass isolation of granules—mitochondria, nuclei, etc. The reason for this is that it is practically impossible, except in a small minority of tissues, to obtain a homogeneous concentration of cells. In the first place, almost all tissues contain, in addition to the typical cellular component, cells of the vascular system, connective tissue cells, and white and red blood cells. Moreover, often the cells of the same type, e.g., hepatic cells, are not of identical chemical composition in closely adjacent parts of an organ. Consequently, it does not follow that a biochemical pattern observed in a particular group of granules is identical with, or even similar to, that of any individual cell type. This can be very simply demonstrated in the case of hepatic cells. Long-chain aldehyde (Feulgen's plasmal), ribonucleic acid, and alkaline phosphatase will occur in the same granule fraction obtained from liver. It would, therefore, be natural to suppose that these three components are bound together in the same granule and may even cooperate in carrying out certain biochemical functions. When, however, the distribution of these three components is studied in tissue sections, it is found that each of them is present to a significant concentration only in some of the hepatic cells. Some hepatic cells may be practically free of any one of these components, some may contain one component, some, two components, and some, three components in significant quantities. If, therefore, all three substances are present on a granule of the same size in the living cells, then it appears that some of the granules contain none of the substances, some, one of the substances, some, two, and some, three. It is thus quite misleading to suppose that all the granules must have all three of these substances, as has been deduced from the procedure of isolation of granules.

It should also be emphasized here that the phenomenon of lack of biological identity of cells, even of the same cell type, illustrates a general weakness of deductions drawn from biochemical studies of extracts. As a general rule, no tissue can be regarded as biologically homogeneous, and deductions made on the biological level after disintegration of tissues must normally be treated with considerable reserve. Only in the case of relatively homogeneous cell preparations, such as those of yeast, bacteria, ova and sperm, can such studies be regarded as referring to a single chemically homogeneous cell population.

In maceration experiments, it is also inevitable that activation and inactivation of enzymes will occur to a degree which may often present formidable difficulties. How this problem can be coped with is not at all clear. There is also the difficulty described by Marjorie Stevenson, that one is tempted to suppose that all enzymes found in a cell must have a function. Dr. Stevenson was inclined to think this must be the case until she found an enzyme in bacteria which could act upon chlorate. She could not believe that this activity could be of any value to the cell since chlorate never appears in its normal environment. One hesitates to agree entirely with this argument: it may well be that the enzyme which acts upon chlorate also acts upon some other substrate which is normally found in the environment, or which from time to time occurs in the environment. And another difficulty in the interpretation of enzyme activities is to know whether any individual enzyme is functioning in connection with a particular physiological activity which is under observation. Indeed, it does not necessarily follow that all the enzymes found in a cell are necessarily functioning at the same time. It seems quite possible that some enzymes may be present in cells at all times, but have a function to fulfill only at exceptional periods in the life of the cell.

When all these experimental hazards and difficulties of interpretation are considered, it must be clear that it will be a long time yet before the results of maceration procedures can be either evaluated or interpreted.

THE SILVER NITRATE-ACETIC ACID TEST FOR ASCORBIC ACID

When tissue is treated by silver nitrate dissolved in acetic acid, it is commonly found that deposits of silver are formed due to reduction of the silver nitrate. It has been claimed that reduction of silver under these conditions is a specific test for ascorbic acid and also that the localization of the silver deposits is a close guide to the localization of ascorbic acid. However, owing to the diffusion factors involved, these conclusions can hardly be true; indeed this system is an excellent example of the complications which are bound to ensue when such chemical studies are attempted on small molecules. Molecules of low molecular weight, such as ascorbic acid, silver nitrate, and probably also the initial reaction product of ascorbic acid with silver nitrate, are highly diffusible. It is thus easy to say much in theory, but it is impossible to prove the precise localization of ascorbic acid by this method. As the silver nitrate-acetic acid mixture diffuses into cells a mixing zone will be established somewhere close to the cell wall in which ascorbic acid and silver nitrate will react. As the reaction proceeds fresh silver nitrate and fresh ascorbic acid will be recruited into the mixing zone until the ascorbic acid supply is exhausted. This interaction in the mixing zone is inevitable with two such highly diffusible substances. Consequently, if ascorbic acid exists in cells as such, it can only be demonstrated in the mixing zone, which is an artefact of fixation. In fact, the silver which is formed by reduction in this procedure is not found in the mixing zone but attached to mitochondria, etc. It is thus clear that either one of three things must be true. The reaction may be truly occurring at the surface of the mitochondria; but if this is true, it is not with free ascorbic acid that the reaction is occurring but a substance bound to the mitochondria so as to render it non-diffusible. An alternative explanation is that the technique does involve a reaction of silver with free ascorbic acid but that the results of the reaction appear adsorbed on surfaces which have a high affinity for the reduced silver and which bear no relationship to the distribution of ascorbic acid in the living cell. A second alternative is that diffusible ascorbic acid is released from the interior of the mitochondria by fixation, and precipitates silver in a mixing zone at the surface of the mitochondria.

Techniques for Cytochemical Demonstration of Enzymes

These techniques usually involve carrying out an enzyme reaction with the intrinsic enzymes of a tissue section or smear, etc., under such conditions that one of the products of the reaction is precipitated. Before results of this type can be evaluated, it is necessary to have answers to a number of questions. These are: (a) How much of the enzyme is destroyed before and during the cytochemical procedure? If destruction occurs, does it occur to an equal degree at all sites or does it occur selectively at certain sites? (b) Is the insoluble reaction product precipitated at the actual site of enzyme reaction, or is it precipitated at sites which have a very high affinity for the reaction product? (c) Is the enzyme in the specimen used for cytochemical study in its physiological position in the material, or has it been redistributed by diffusion processes? Studies which do not provide answers to these questions must be discarded. It is, no doubt, true that some of the methods now used to study the distribution of enzymes do, in fact, demonstrate the correct site of the enzyme; it is equally true that there are other instances in which the information provided is greatly misleading.

The Feulgen Technique for Nucleic Acid

In this technique tissues are heated at 60° with normal hydrochloric acid for 5 minutes or more, the precise time varying with the fixative which is used and the nature of the specimen. This procedure splits off purine from the deoxy sugar nucleic acid, so that, when the material is subsequently treated with reduced fuchsin, a violet Schiff's base is formed. The procedure of hydrolysis, however, tends also to make nucleic acids diffusible, probably by reducing the molecular weight, as was suggested by Stedman and Stedman. That this was likely to be the case has been implicit in results known for many years. For example, Bauer showed that, when a fixative like formaldehyde is used, or acetic alcohol, the intensity of the reaction reaches a peak after, say, 5 or 10 minutes of hydrolysis. Further hydrolysis rather rapidly diminishes the amount of nucleic acid which can be demonstrated in a section. On the other hand, if a heavy metal such as mercury is present in the fixative, the hydrolysis may profitably be more prolonged, with an increase in the intensity of reaction and no evidence of loss of material even after 30 minutes' hydrolysis. It seems clear from these observations of Bauer that the Feulgen hydrolysis, in some way at least, must be making it possible for nucleic acid to diffuse, and that it may be more firmly anchored in the section by conversion into the salt of a heavy metal such as mercury before the hydrolysis is carried out. If the hydrolysis makes it possible for nucleic acid to diffuse out of the section, then it may also be possible for it to diffuse into the section. In consequence, there must remain some slight doubt as to whether the details of the picture revealed by the Feulgen technique are not to some degree invalidated by diffusion artefacts. It is to be regretted that no attempt has been made to study carefully the extent to which diffusion does, in fact, take place during the Feulgen procedure.

It would be of considerable value if a film could be made, by means of ultraviolet light, of changes in the distribution of nucleic acid in cells which are undergoing chemical fixation, and the results so obtained compared with the results obtained by freeze-drying, following which a study should be made of the course of distribution of ultraviolet-absorbing material in the same specimen, preferably by filming the cells during hydrolysis. It seems likely that the difficulties in such a problem caused by prolonged exposure to ultraviolet light can be minimized by using a newly developed instrument, the television microscope, which requires much less intensity of light than does a direct photograph with a photographic film.

The Use of Absorption Spectra

Practically all cytochemical methods involve at one stage or another the observation of the absorption spectrum of a specimen. It is, therefore, necessary to bear in mind certain problems which constitute limitations in the interpretation of such studies even when the instrumental problems have been solved.

These are:

1. The study of absorption spectra can provide evidence of the presence of only certain chemical groups in a particular site: this is not in itself conclusive evidence of the presence of any one given chemical substance.

2. When two groups are shown to exist in the same position in a cell, it is not normally possible from studies of absorption spectrum to determine whether these groups occur in the same molecule or in different molecules.

3. The spectrum of a molecule may be rather markedly affected by the adjacent or neighbouring molecules. Thus Caspersson states that the absorption spectrum of nucleic acid is altered to a significant degree by the combination of nucleic acid with basic proteins. Fox and Danielli have shown that the absorption maximum of astacine is shifted from the yellow into the red by adsorption at an oil-water interface. R. A. Peters has shown that a similar reversible change occurs with astaxanthine; when astaxanthine is combined with certain proteins the color is blue, and when it is removed from this combination the colour is red. An extreme example of this type of behaviour is found with haem, the spectrum of which varies in a very characteristic manner according to whether it is combined with the appropriate protein which gives, for example, a haemoglobin, a catalase, a peroxidase, a cytochrome, or a cytochrome oxidase.

4. All quantitative studies on the absorption spectrum of different parts of the cell need to be corrected for loss of light caused by scattering in the specimen, and must be corrected, also, for the degree of orientation of the absorbing molecules and their state of aggregation in the specimen. Furthermore it must be demonstrated that the Beer-Lambert law is obeyed.

THE USE OF ENZYMES IN CYTOCHEMICAL REACTIONS

A procedure which is rather commonly used is to allow a purified enzyme preparation to act upon a specimen. For example, Brachet has suggested that stains should be used to identify the site of ribonucleic acid and that the presence of this acid should be checked by the use of ribonuclease which should remove all staining material. Such procedures involving enzymes do provide additional circumstantial evidence of the existence of the components constituting their substrates in particular parts of cells. However, final proof can never be obtained by this type of technique for the following reasons:

1. It is never possible to establish that a particular enzyme is pure. It is, of course, possible to show that a particular enzyme such as ribonuclease is lacking in activity, say, toward certain peptide bonds or certain forms of linkage of sugar molecules. But it is never feasible to show that a preparation is lacking in ability to split all the various types of bonds in substances which might be involved in anchoring a dye. Consequently, there is always

the hazard in the use of enzyme preparations that the loss of a stained substance from a cell has been produced by some enzyme action other than that which it was intended should occur.

2. Even if one neglects the hazard of contamination by other enzymes, there are considerable difficulties in interpreting the removal of substances from sections by enzyme action. For example, it is possible that a structure composed mainly of nucleic acid could be protected from the action of the enzyme ribonuclease by quite small quantities of protein. Even a monolayer of protein might be sufficient to prevent access of the enzyme to its substrate. Conversely, a structure consisting almost entirely of protein, but held together and held in the section by a fine matrix of ribonucleic acid, might well be removed by ribonuclease although the nucleic acid constituted an extremely small fraction of the structure as a whole.

3. Many of the components even in a fixed preparation are not totally indiffusible and will migrate from the fixed section if a suitable adsorbing reagent is available. For example, Catcheside and Holmes have shown that ribonucleic acid may be removed from chromosomes by what appears to be egg albumin, supposedly an inert protein.

REFERENCES

Bauer. 1933. *Zeit. f. mikr.-anat. Forsch., 33,* 143.
Brachet. 1940. *C. r. soc. biol. Paris, 133,* 90.
　　　 1944. *Embryologie chimique* (Masson, Paris).
Callan. 1952. *Symp. Soc. Exp. Biol., 6* (in press).
Caspersson. 1950. *Cell Growth and Cell Function* (Norton, New York).
Catcheside and Holmes. 1947. *Symp. Soc. Exp. Biol., 1,* 225.
Chayen. 1952. *Symp. Soc. Exp. Biol., VI* (in press).
Danielli. 1946. *Nature, 157,* 755.
Dounce. 1948. Personal Communication.
Feulgen and Rossenbeck. 1924. *Zeit. f. physiol. Chemie, 135,* 203.
Fischer. 1899. *Fixierung, Färbung und Bau des Protoplasmas* (Gustav Fischer, Jena).
Fox and Danielli. 1941. *Biochem. J., 35,* 13, 88.
Hardy. 1899. *J. Physiol., 24,* 158.
Holter. 1946. *Nature, 158,* 917.
Lison. 1936. *Histochimie Animale* (Gauthier-Villars, Paris).
Mugard. 1953. *Quart. J. Micros. Sci.* (in press).
Shapiro. 1939. *Cold Spring Harbor Symposia, 8,* 406.
Stedman and Stedman. 1943. *Nature, 152,* 267.

CHAPTER 2

FIXATION PROCEDURES

Almost any tissue which is to be subjected to a cytochemical procedure must first be fixed. The ideal result of fixation would be to have an exact replica of the living tissue with each of the molecules present in the original specimen in its original place, and with no foreign molecules present. This is clearly an impossible ideal to achieve. In general, fixation can succeed only in maintaining the large molecules, such as proteins, nucleic acid, and carbohydrates, in approximately their original positions. In the case of the proteins, a considerable proportion of the molecules are irreversibly changed. Indeed, if fixation is to produce a specimen which will be satisfactory for any length of time, the fixing agent used must effect two phenomena: it must precipitate proteins and it must directly or indirectly greatly restrict enzyme activity. It is not necessary that the fixative should denature the proteins. For example, when a heavy metal is the basis of a fixative, it precipitates the proteins effectively but does not necessarily denature them. Similarly, it is not necessarily the case that an enzyme should be directly inactivated; it may be sufficient that it should be rendered indiffusible by being captured by a matrix of another protein. But if the enzyme systems of a cell are not, by one method or another, prevented from displaying their normal activity, the proteolytic and other hydrolytic enzymes rapidly destroy the integrity of the tissue.

Fixation is commonly carried out by the action of chemical agents alone. Occasionally freeze-drying is used, but in the past this has been somewhat uncommon.

A major problem in the choice of fixative is presented by the fact that, while a considerable amount of change must be brought about in the specimen to render it insoluble in water and to prevent enzyme activity, it is, nevertheless, necessary that the group which is to be studied cytochemically shall not be affected to any serious degree. The choice of fixing agent has to be made with the careful consideration of its effect upon the group which is to be studied. It commonly happens, therefore, that what to the cytologist has been the best type of fixative is not available to the cytochemist. The common ingredients of fixatives include strong oxidizing agents, such as osmic acid and chromic acid; strong reducing agents, such as formaldehyde and formic acid; cross-linking substances, such as formaldehyde and osmic acid; and acids, bases, and heavy metals which can precipitate such substances as nucleic acids and proteins. In addition, anhydrous fluids such as alcohol and acetic acid are quite commonly used; they exercise their effect very largely as denaturing agents. The anhydrous solvents cause denaturation mainly by breaking up the lipoid adhesions which assist in maintaining the native state in many proteins. Table I sets out

TABLE I

The action of various chemical reagents commonly employed as components of fixatives upon chemical groups in tissue sections. + indicates that a group is unaltered by a reagent. − indicates that it is unsafe to use this component if it is desired to keep a particular group intact.

	$CHOH$	NH_2	SH	CO_2H	Histidine	Tryptophane	Tyrosine	Sugar	Aldehyde	Nucleic Acid
Formaldehyde	+	−	?	+	+	+	+	+	+	?
Alcohol	+	+	+	?	+	+	+	+	+	?
Acetic acid	−	−	−	?	?	?	−	?	+	?
Mercury	+	+	−	?	+	+	+	+	+	?
Osmic acid	?	?	−	?	?	−	?	−	−	?
Dichromate	−	?	−	+	?	−	?	−	−	?
Acetone	+	+	+	+	+	+	+	?	+	+
Pyridine	+	+	?	+	+	+	+	+	+	+
Picric acid	+	+	?	?	+	?	+	+	+	+

a list of fixing agents and indicates their action upon various groups which may be of interest to the cytologist. It will be seen that there are many of the ingredients of the better chemical fixatives which commonly should be avoided. For example, if a study is to be made of NH_2 groups or of phenols such as tyrosine, acetic acid in anhydrous solution must be avoided because of the danger of acetylation of the groups concerned. If

SH groups, or sugars, are to be studied, oxidizing agents such as osmic acid must be avoided. If amino groups are to be studied, formaldehyde must be avoided, etc. When enzymes are of interest, the limitations are even more severe. A substance like osmic acid must be avoided completely.

During the action of chemical fixatives, artefacts may arise due to precipitation, diffusion, and adsorption, and also due to activation and inactivation of enzymes. The endeavour with regard to precipitation is not to avoid precipitation—indeed the whole object of fixation is to secure proper precipitation—but to see that the size of the particles precipitated is less than the resolving power of the light used. Diffusion and adsorption artefacts present a source of great difficulty. One method of detecting these artefacts is to use a variety of fixing agents of widely different physical properties. For example, if the same structure or distribution of a substance is observed with fixatives which are acid, neutral, basic, and anhydrous, it is rather unlikely that the observed cytochemical pattern is an artefact. On the other hand, the use of a wide variety of fixatives is not an absolutely safe guarantee against the formation of artefacts. Moreover, it frequently happens, especially when enzymes are being studied, that the range of fixing agents which can be used without destruction of enzymes is too restricted to permit this method of detection of artefacts.

When the cytochemical method is applied to the analysis of a physiological activity, e.g., enzyme action, it is very difficult to assign a precise significance to the degree of activity which is observed in the fixed preparation. If one knows the extent of enzyme activity at a particular part of the preparation and can be sure this has not been modified by the fixation procedure, it is still not possible to estimate the degree to which this enzyme is active under physiological conditions. Before that degree of activity can be determined, it is necessary to have a precise knowledge of the physio-chemical environment of the enzyme under physiological conditions. This means knowing what other colloids are present in the immediate environment of the enzyme, since enzyme activation is greatly affected by the presence of other colloidal molecules or surfaces on which the enzyme may be adsorbed. Then it is necessary to know the hydrogen-ion concentration, the ionic strength, the substrate concentration, the reaction-product concentration and the concentrations of activators and inhibitors in the immediate vicinity of the enzyme. With the exception of one or two substances, such as cytochrome oxidase and muscle hemoglobin, it must be admitted that we are not as yet in a position to determine the exact degree of activity of any enzyme in a particular site in the cell. The use of chemical substances to effect fixation has been disadvantageous in cytochemical work, from a purely chemical point of view. It also has many disadvantages in that it is extremely difficult to detect artefacts due to diffusion and adsorption. In view of this, there can be no doubt but that the method of choice is freeze-drying. However, it must be emphasized that, unless freeze-drying is carried out with rigid attention to detail, the artefacts which may arise can be even more serious than those found with chemical fixation. The method of freeze-drying was introduced by Altmann in 1890, and greatly developed by Gersh. The principle involved is to solidify the material by plunging a small piece into a fluid at a very low temperature. The material is then placed in a chamber which is evacuated, and the water is then pumped off while the specimen is kept frozen solid. When all the water has been removed, the specimen may be embedded in wax and subjected to sectioning, etc.

The apparatus which has been used in the past for this purpose has suffered from a number of deficiencies. It has been delicate, containing a great deal of glass tubing; it has not been easily possible to process considerable quantities of material; mechanical refrigeration has considerably restricted the range of drying temperatures which can be used and also is frequently unreliable; and, not least, must be mentioned the fact that such apparatus is expensive to build or buy. Mr. L. G. Bell and I have therefore developed, in collaboration with W. Edwards and Co., a freeze-drying apparatus which is sufficiently robust and inexpensive to be suitable for routine work in almost any laboratory. Figure 1 illustrates the principle of the drying unit. The procedure is to fix the specimen by plunging it into isopentane which has been cooled in liquid nitrogen. It is desirable to avoid liquid air as a cooling agent, since, if for any reason the isopentane and liquid air become mixed, a violent explosion will ensue. It is necessary to use intermediate cooling agents

such as isopentane, rather than plunge the specimen directly
into liquid air or liquid nitrogen, since, if the specimen is directly in contact with liquid air or nitrogen, gas bubbles form

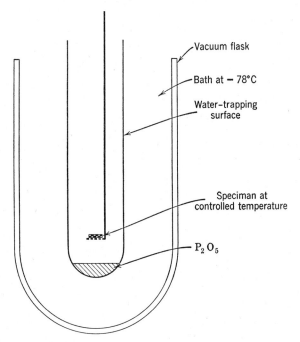

FIG. 1. Illustrating principle of new-type freeze-dryer. Former freeze-
dryers pumped the water off into a P_2O_5 trap. In the present type the
water is trapped on the walls of the evacuated tube, which are maintained
at $-78°$ C. until the specimen is dry. Then on warming the tube the
water is returned by the P_2O_5 at the tube base. During the drying process
the specimen is warmed by a thermostatically controlled heater to a defined temperature, usually $-40°$ C. When the vacuum is maintained by
a two-stage rotary pump, drying requires about 2 days. If a diffusion
pump is used, backed by a rotary pump, the drying time can be reduced
to 6–10 hours for a specimen not more than 1 mm. thick. But there is
usually no advantage in reducing the drying time to this extent.

around the specimen, due to vaporization of the liquid. As a
consequence, the specimen is insulated from the liquid air and
cools very much more slowly than when good thermal contact
is maintained between the cooling agent and the specimen.
Isopentane freezes at approximately $-160°$. When an optimal

result is required, it is sometimes desirable to achieve a somewhat lower temperature. This can be done by using a eutectic mixture of propane and isopentane, or propane and butane, instead of isopentane.

The drying chamber which we have developed has an easily demountable head, attached to which are the racks which carry the specimens. The procedure which we use is to surround the drying chamber with an acetone-solid CO_2 mixture which maintains the drying unit at approximately $-78°$ C. The demountable head is placed with the specimen racks in liquid nitrogen. When the specimen has been frozen in the cooled pentane, the racks are lifted out of the liquid nitrogen, the specimen placed on the racks, and the unit placed in the drying chamber and evacuated. From the time the specimen is lifted out of the pentane bath to the time when it is placed in the drying chamber at $-78°$, only a few seconds elapse.

The general procedure which we use is then to dry the material for two or three days. The walls of the drying chamber are maintained at $-78°$, and the drying chamber is arranged so that the racks containing the specimens are electrically heated to a defined temperature, variable between $-60°$ C. and $-10°$ C. as required. Under these conditions the water vapor from the specimen sublimes from the specimen to the walls of the drying tube. This involves a very short vapor path. Consequently, the pumping unit has no load placed upon it. It is not necessary for the water vapor to be pumped over into a water trap as has commonly been the case in previous drying units. The pump is used merely to maintain the basic low pressure, and the water vapor sublimes from the specimen to the sides of the drying chamber. When the specimen has been sufficiently dried, the temperature of the drying chamber is allowed to rise to room temperature. When this occurs, the water vapor rapidly sublimes into a phosphorous pentoxide trap. If desired, this latter stage can be avoided by having a phosphorous pentoxide component in the drying chamber itself. But we have encountered no difficulty with this procedure of subliming the water from the specimen to a more highly cooled surface a short distance away, followed by a rapid distillation of this water to a trap, carried out at room temperature when the specimen is already dried. The apparatus has been constructed so that it consists of metal tubing, and, as the water vapor is not being pumped into a trap at the low-temperature stage, it has not been necessary to incorporate a diffusion pump, since a two-stage rotary pump can do all that is required. The specimen temperature is defined by a thermostatic device, and the temperature may be checked by a thermocouple which is associated with each thermostat. As the apparatus does not involve mechanical refrigeration, it can run indefinitely without overhauling. Since there is no load thrown on the pump, it is possible to have a number of drying tubes separately linked to the same pump. We are at present using a system of four separate drying tubes, each of which contains two or three trays of specimens. Each drying tube can be opened and shut independently of the other tubes, so that material can be processed in considerable quantity.

Provided that the specimen is not to go into an aqueous solution or any other highly polar solvent such as glycerol or formic acid, the specimen may be embedded, sectioned, and examined without any further treatment. We customarily allow the specimen to come up to room temperature in the drying chamber, then place it in an infiltration unit containing degassed wax. The apparatus is evacuated and the wax melted and run onto the specimen, which may then be embedded and sectioned by the usual procedure. Provided that the specimen is allowed to come to room temperature, we have not encountered any difficulty with condensation of water vapor from the air as the dried specimen is transferred from the drying unit to the infiltration unit. It may be necessary under conditions of high humidity to warm the specimen to above room temperature before transfer. If so, the specimen can readily be warmed to a sufficient degree by the heating unit of the drying chamber. Alternatively, the drying tray may be replaced by a bath containing a little solidified degassed wax. When the drying is completed, the temperature of the wax can then be raised slightly above its melting point by the heating unit of the drying chamber; infiltration of wax then occurs without moving the specimen.

If the material to be studied must be subjected to aqueous or other highly polar solvents, a fixative procedure must be used after freeze-drying. The reason for this is that freeze-drying preserves most of the proteins and other substances present in the cell in such a normal condition that they readily dissolve in many polar substances. A fixation procedure may be applied after drying and before embedding, or it may be applied to individual sections after embedding in wax. We are at present experimenting with the possibility of fixatives which can be used as vapors to act directly upon the specimen after it has been dried. Gases such as formaldehyde, carbon suboxide, hydrochloric acid, and osmic acid have potentialities for such a procedure. Most of our work, however, has involved material which has been embedded and sectioned after freeze-drying. The sections are then flattened either by using a non-aqueous solvent such as alcohol, or by flattening the section on mercury. Then, after the wax has been removed from the section, the latter can be subjected to the fixing action of alcohol and other anhydrous solutions which may contain acids, bases, heavy metals, etc., as desired. As a result of such procedures, the specimens become sufficiently insoluble in polar solvents.

It is of interest to calculate the time relationships in freeze-drying and in fixation by chemical agents. Studies of cell permeability show that when cells 2 microns in thickness are placed in a solution of a solvent such as ethyl alcohol, the concentration of alcohol inside the cell reaches about 50 percent of that of the outside in about 10 seconds. Thus, if individual cells of this size were brought into direct contact with alcohol, the concentration of alcohol would reach about 50 percent in about 10 seconds and fixation would become effective in about 10–20 seconds. But most of the material with which we deal is in tissue sections which are much thicker than 2 microns. For a thin slice of tissue 2 millimeters in diameter placed in alcohol, the time required for fixation to become effective would be approximately $\sqrt{1000}$ times longer, i.e., on the average with this material it would require roughly 330 seconds or more before fixation becomes really effective with a chemical fixative. When more slowly penetrating materials, such as heavy metals, are used as fixatives, the time for effective fixation may be considerably increased.

The time taken for effective fixation to be accomplished by the technique described above, using isopentane, can be roughly ascertained by plunging a specimen containing a thermocouple into the pentane. It is found in this way that the temperature in the centre of a 2-millimeter section of tissue falls below $-50°$ in less than 10 seconds and falls below $-170°$ in less than 30 seconds. It is thus probable that a 2-millimeter piece of material is effectively solidified in two or three seconds, compared with a minimum of 330 seconds which are necessary when a rapidly penetrating chemical fixative is used. Thus freezing in a fluid at liquid air temperature is immensely more rapid than any chemical agent can possibly be. If the water in the specimen remained liquid for some time after cooling in pentane, diffusion would nevertheless be very greatly reduced as a result of the great increase in viscosity caused by lowering the temperature. After 3 seconds the viscosity of the water in the specimen would be more than 100 times greater than that of the specimen at room temperature, and, after 10 seconds in the bath, the viscosity would be of the order of 10^6 times that in the same specimen at room temperature. In fact, the resistance to diffusion is probably much greater than this, owing to the formation of ice in the specimen.

However, even with this very great speed of fixation, it is possible that diffusion artefacts may occur when the distribution of small molecules within a cell is under consideration. Diffusion artefacts will be detectable if significant changes can take place in the distribution of a substance over distances roughly of the order of 0.2 micron. If a substance of the molecular weight of ethyl alcohol were present in a region of a cell, such as a mitochondrion, approximately 0.2 micron in thickness, in the few seconds required for cooling to $-50°$ an almost complete loss of substance from the mitochondria could occur if the effect of cooling were to make the substance suddenly as diffusible as is ethyl alcohol. Significant and indeed very serious diffusion artefacts might, therefore, arise with small molecules and small ions, even with the rapid fixation obtained with isopentane cooled with liquid nitrogen. Even with large molecules, significant artefacts could arise. Thus, with a protein having a molecular weight of 20,000, about 1 percent could be lost from a region 0.2 micron thick in 1 second, and for a substance of a molecular weight of 10^6 the loss could be less than 0.1 percent. It is clear, from calculation of the rise in viscosity as the temperature falls in the specimen, that significant diffusion cannot occur after liquid-air temperatures have been reached, even with a rapidly diffusing substance such as ethyl alcohol.

It thus appears that freeze-drying, or rather freezing in cool isopentane, produces an effective fixation in a time which is of the order of 1 percent of the time required for the effective action of a chemical fixative, when a specimen of about 2 millimeters in thickness is considered. In making these calculations, it has been assumed that the fixative moves into the specimen by thermal diffusion only. In some cases the rate of penetration of a chemical fixing agent may be somewhat increased or reduced by shrinking, cracking, or swelling of the specimen. But it is highly improbable that the time for effective fixation by chemical substances falls much below 100 times that required for effective fixation by cooling, even with the maximum rate of penetration which may be achieved when an accidental flow of fixative is procured by cracking.

In theory it is possible that serious diffusion artefacts may develop during fixation even with the freeze-drying technique. This is certain to be the case with small molecules and small ions, and it is improbable with substances of high molecular weight. Substances of low molecular weight tend to be uniformly distributed in cells by thermal agitation. Opposed to the effect of thermal agitation are adsorption and other more complicated activities of the cell. The normal distribution of a low-molecular-weight substance represents a compromise between these tendencies. As the temperature falls the dispersing effect of thermal agitation declines correspondingly and the relative importance of adsorption forces increases; since the diffusion time for small molecules is bound to be small compared with the cooling time, this abnormal dominance of absorption forces must inevitably produce redistribution of small molecules. Diffusion artefacts of this type cannot be avoided. On the other hand, with high-molecular-weight molecules adsorption is normally much greater than for small molecules, and the diffusion time is much larger. Consequently, with freeze-drying, diffusion artefacts are not likely to occur with molecules of high molecular weight. But with chemical fixation the balance is thrown heavily in favour of diffusion artefacts in two ways. First, the action time of chemical fixation is about a hundred or more times longer than with freezing fixation, so that artefacts have much longer to develop. Secondly, chemical fixatives are inherently rather violent reagents and inevitably break up most of the adsorption systems of cells, and so they temporarily render many molecules more diffusible than is normal. Consequently, diffusion artefacts must be expected, even with large molecules, when chemical fixation is used.

It cannot be too strongly emphasized that, although freeze-drying presents such a great advantage over chemical fixation, artefacts may nevertheless arise with some types of molecules during the fixation process. Also small molecules such as inorganic ions and sugars may diffuse to a significant degree in the wax used for embedding. This must be a subject for future investigation.

Until the degree of diffusion during fixation and infiltration is ascertained, it will not be possible to tell whether the localization of small molecules is reliable, even when freeze-drying, followed by embedding in wax, is used as the basis of technique. Thus most of the results obtained by microincineration have involved specimens infiltrated in wax. Whether the distribution of sodium, potassium, etc., found by this technique is correct cannot be determined until it is known what artefacts develop during fixation, infiltration, and embedding in wax.

Dr. L. G. Bell has also found that artefacts may arise when gels are subjected to the freeze-drying technique. Although one knows that, when examined with a microscope, a gelatin gel is homogeneous, a section of gelatin gel prepared by the freeze-drying technique is not homogeneous. It appears that when weak gels are dried and forced into wax, cracking and contraction occur so as to give rise to a somewhat fibrous material. The fibres are, however, artefacts.

From time to time it has been questioned whether the fact that, after a specimen has been dried, it must normally be subjected to a fixing agent does not deprive one of a great deal of the advantage which is gained from the great speed with which diffusion is restricted by cooling at room temperatures. However, there is probably very little loss in efficiency. Once a specimen has been effectively dehydrated, most of the molecules of molecular weight greater than, say, 1000, are bound into a solid unit which will break down only if the specimen is passed into a polar solvent; e.g., the protein molecules and the nucleic acid molecules are held in positions from which they cannot diffuse to a significant extent. If a fixing agent is applied to such molecules once they are held in this way, they will be permanently fixed in their normal position, apart from such cracking and contraction as may occur. Artefacts due to cracking and contraction are, of course, rather readily detected in a specimen.

In conclusion, Plates I and II illustrate two of the types of artefacts which occur in chemical fixation. Plate I, Fig. A shows the type of distribution of glycogen which is normally obtained in liver with chemical fixation. Figure B shows the distribution of glycogen obtained when freeze-drying is used as the fixing technique. There is a striking contrast between the two results, and it is evident that, as a result of the forces set up by diffusion processes during the action of a chemical fixative, glycogen in a cell is forced out of its normal position. Plate II, Fig. A shows an ultraviolet photograph of rat Walker sarcoma fixed in Carnoy's fixative (acetic acid and alcohol) which is thought by cytologists to be one of the best fixatives for the demonstration of nucleic acid in such material. In this preparation the contrast in the resting nuclei is quite striking, and surrounding the metaphase plate there is a clear zone containing practically no material absorbing ultraviolet light. Plate II, Fig. B shows quite different results obtained by freeze-drying. Contrast in the resting nuclei is much less than in Plate II, Fig. A and there is no clear zone surrounding the metaphase plate. It is obvious that in the action of a chemical fixative considerable diffusion may occur of a substance, probably ribonucleic acid, which absorbs light in the ultraviolet. After this demonstration, it seems hardly necessary to emphasize the desirability of using the freeze-drying technique whenever it is available.

Plate III illustrates the quality of the results which may be obtained by cytochemical methods subsequent to freeze-drying.

REFERENCES

Altmann. 1890. *Die Elementarenorganismen und ihre Bezeihungen zu den Zellen* (von Veit, Leipzig).

Bell. 1952. *International Review of Cytology, 1,* 35.

Gersh. 1932. *Anat. Rec., 53,* 309.

Gersh, Sylvén, Sjostrand, and Bell. 1952. *Freezing and Drying* (Institute of Biology, London).

CHAPTER 3

STUDIES ON ALKALINE PHOSPHATASE

The localization of enzymes in particular parts of cells is one of the general problems of cytochemistry which must be largely solved before it will be possible to make full use of the body of knowledge of enzymes which is being built up by the biochemists. Alkaline phosphatase is a particularly favorable enzyme for experimenting on possibilities in this field, since it is rather resistant to experimental procedures and thus makes readily accessible study of all the various artefacts which arise in the cytochemistry of enzymes—with, of course, the exception of destruction of enzyme due to the sensitivity of the enzyme itself to experimental procedures.

Alkaline phosphatase is usually defined as an enzyme which splits phosphate esters according to the following equation

$$ROPO_3H_2 \rightleftharpoons ROH + HOPO_3H_2$$

with a pH optimum in the vicinity of 9.3. It is not specific for any special group of phosphomonoesters, but, on the other hand, it will hydrolyze only the monoesters.

The first histochemical study of alkaline phosphatase was published by Robison in 1923. He showed that, if a thick section of hypertrophic cartilage is immersed in a solution containing an ester of phosphoric acid and calcium, a precipitate of calcium phosphate occurs in the section at sites which may be revealed by staining with silver. He showed that the calcium phosphate deposits are found only in those regions in which primary bone formation is occurring, and he was thus able to establish a close relationship between the histological occurrence of alkaline phosphatase in cartilage and calcification of cartilage.

No further advance occurred until 1939, when Gomori and Takamatsu practically simultaneously published papers in which they showed that the type of technique developed by

Robison could be extended down to the cytological level. This work of Gomori and of Takamatsu gave a great new impetus to the study of the cytological distribution of enzymes. Their work, however, suffered from the disadvantage that they had not studied most of the major physico-chemical hazards and problems which may arise in the cytological study of enzymes. These problems may, as was indicated in Chapter 1, be formulated as follows:

1. How much phosphatase is destroyed by the experimental procedures? And if phosphatase is destroyed, is it destroyed selectively at certain sites in the tissue, or is it destroyed to the same extent at all the sites at which it occurs?

2. Does the precipitate of calcium phosphate indicate the true site of the alkaline phosphatase, or does it merely indicate sites in the tissues which have a high affinity for calcium phosphate?

3. Is the enzyme in a fixed section in its physiologically normal position?

Until answers can be given to these three questions, it is impossible to place any reliance on results obtained by this technique. This chapter will consist of a study of the methods by which these questions may be answered, and a consideration of some of the results which have been obtained in cases where satisfactory answers can be provided to these questions.

General Technical Considerations

It may be noted that to obtain optimal results, i.e., results with a minimum of fixation artefacts and a minimum of destruction of enzyme, the freeze-drying technique is by far the best. Where freeze-drying is not available, one may fix in 80 percent alcohol, and then take the block after 2 hours into absolute alcohol, in which the material must remain for at least 2 hours. After the treatment with absolute alcohol, the block may be either taken down to water and used for cutting frozen sections or cleared by passage through such agents as cedarwood oil, methyl benzoate, or benzene. It may then be infiltrated and embedded in wax, at a temperature which should be kept below 60° C. If the material is embedded, sections may be cut by the usual procedures, flattened on distilled water, the wax removed with xylol, after which the sections are taken into absolute alcohol and then into 0.1 percent collodion, from which they should pass into 50 percent alcohol, then into 25 percent alcohol and distilled water. The section should remain at least 5 minutes in the distilled water so that small amounts of pre-formed calcium phosphate may be removed from the section.

The sections are then incubated in a mixture containing a phosphate ester and calcium. As the enzyme splits off phosphate from the ester precipitation of calcium phosphate occurs in the sections. When studying tissues of unknown phosphatase concentration, I have found it convenient to incubate trial sections for 2 hours and for 20 hours. With the information provided by these trial sections, it is possible to determine the optimal periods for which sections should be incubated to discover the detail of distribution of enzyme in the different sites in the specimen. It is always advisable, when a detailed study is being made after the preliminary trials, to use a series of times of incubation, e.g., for mammalian kidney, 5, 10, 20, 40, and 80 minutes. The composition of the incubation mixture which has been used for most of the studies reported here has been:

	Milliliters
2 percent sodium veronal	20
2 percent sodium glycerophosphate	20
2 percent calcium nitrate	10
2 percent magnesium chloride	2
Water	48
	100

In some of the earlier work which is included in this chapter, magnesium was omitted. Magnesium is included to act as an activator of the enzyme. It is not always necessary but will often enhance enzyme activity.

After incubation, the section should be washed in 2 percent calcium nitrate solution for a few minutes, then taken into 1 percent cobalt nitrate solution. This converts the calcium phosphate into cobalt phosphate. The section is then washed in distilled water to remove the excess cobalt nitrate, and then placed in an ammonium sulfide solution, which converts the cobalt phosphate into cobalt sulfide, which is black. The sections may then be mounted in the usual manner. To avoid loss of material from sections due to slight acidity in the washing medium, the calcium nitrate solution, cobalt nitrate solution, and distilled water should each have an addition of 0.5 milliliter of sodium veronal per 100 milliliters of solution.

The method just described localizes the phosphate end of the ester. A method published by Menten, Junge, and Green in 1944 and Danielli in 1946 localizes the alcoholic end of the molecule as an insoluble diazo dye. In this method the incubation medium contains a phenol phosphate and a diazonium hydroxide. Phenol phosphates do not react with diazonium hydroxides. But, in the presence of phosphatase, the ester is split, giving rise to phenol, which reacts very rapidly with the diazonium hydroxide. By a correct choice of phenol and diazonium hydroxide, it can be arranged that the reaction product of the phenol and diazonium hydroxide is very insoluble in water and is therefore precipitated in the section in the vicinity of the enzyme.

The medium which is conveniently used for these experiments consists of a phenol phosphate solution in sodium veronal, containing 0.1 gram of phenol phosphate suspended or dissolved in 50 milliliters of 2 percent sodium veronal solution. To this is added, just before use, 25 milliliters of diazonium hydroxide solution containing 0.2 percent of diazonium hydroxide. The diazonium hydroxide solutions may be prepared by the methods given by Saunders (1936). The diazonium hydroxide may be kept for a period of hours in the hydrochloric acid solution in which it is prepared, or often for more prolonged periods as a stabilized compound in solid form. Just before use it is brought to pH 9.2–9.3 by the use of thymol blue as an indicator, and then mixed with phenol phosphate solution and filtered, keeping the temperature between 6 and 8° C. throughout the operation. After filtration the slides may be placed in the medium. Many diazonium hydroxides decompose rather rapidly under these conditions, and it may be necessary to change the incubation medium every 20 minutes to obtain optimal results.

Some workers have had difficulty in using this technique, through paying insufficient attention to the adjustment of the pH of the diazonium hydroxide solution. The diazonium hydroxide reacts with the indicator thymol blue, which is itself a phenol, to give another indicator substance which has a color change very similar to that of thymol blue, but with which the color change occurs only in much more strongly alkaline solutions. Consequently, unless due care is used, the pH of the diazonium hydroxide solution is not adjusted to pH 9.2 but to a strongly alkaline value. When the tissue sections are immersed in this strongly alkaline solution, the phosphatase is rapidly destroyed and, of course, no cytochemical reaction occurs. To avoid this difficulty drops of indicator should be placed in a white tile, and to one of these should be added a drop of the diazonium hydroxide solution. When the diazonium hydroxide solution is at approximately pH 9.2–9.3, on addition of the drop the mixture will initially turn to the appropriate blue-grey color, which will then rapidly fade. If the solution remains blue, the diazonium hydroxide solution is too alkaline.

Loss of Enzyme Due to Experimental Techniques

Under this general heading will be included losses due to diffusion of substances out of tissue sections at various stages of the procedure, and also loss of enzyme due to inactivation.

EFFECT OF FIXATION

The fixative originally recommended by Takamatsu and Gomori was 80 percent alcohol. The effect of this 80 percent alcohol on phosphatase activity was studied on the test-tube level by the usual biochemical procedure for the study of alkaline phosphatase. Pieces of rat kidney were ground up in a mortar and the activities of aliquots determined (a) without fixation, (b) after 2 hours' exposure to 80 percent alcohol. No significant difference could be found between the phosphatase activity of the two samples. Further experiments were carried out (c) with 10 μ frozen sections cut from a block of unfixed rat kidney and 10 μ frozen sections which had been fixed for 2 hours in 80 percent alcohol and 6 hours in absolute alcohol. The sectioned material was ground as before and studied by the biochemical procedure. Again no difference could be found between the enzyme content of the fixed and unfixed material. It may therefore be concluded that no significant loss of alkaline phosphatase occurs as a result of fixation in alcohol. Consequently it was possible to use the deposition of cobalt sulfide in frozen sections from alcohol-fixed blocks as a standard for estimating roughly enzyme losses caused by paraffin embedding, etc.

THE EFFECT OF EMBEDDING, ETC.

Since alcohol does not destroy alkaline phosphatase to a significant degree, frozen sections from alcohol-fixed blocks may be used to control the effect of later procedures. Sections were cut from a paraffin block and incubated for 0, 10, 20, 40, 80, 160, and 320 minutes in the glycerophosphate incubation mixture given above. This series of sections was compared with a similar series prepared as frozen sections from an alcohol-fixed block for the same periods. The comparison showed that a considerable loss of activity occurred during infiltration and embedding. In a number of such experiments it was estimated that the loss of enzyme activity may amount to 75 percent of the total. The loss, however, did not appear to be localized but occurred to the same extent, as far as may be distinguished by the eye, in all sites in which the enzyme occurs. If the fixation, infiltration, etc., were carried out under anaerobic conditions, a much greater destruction of enzyme activity was found to occur.

THE CRITICAL TIME LIMITS OF OPERATIONS

Preliminary experiments suggested that loss of apparent enzyme activity might be occurring in some stages of the procedure. Two groups of experiments were therefore carried through to see to what extent this could be controlled. Three blocks of material were fixed in 80 percent alcohol and then taken to absolute alcohol after 2 hours. From one of these blocks a series of frozen sections was prepared. The second block was allowed to spend 2 hours in each of the dehydrating and clearing agents and infiltrated with wax for 8 hours at 60° C. The third block was allowed to spend 24 hours in each dehydrating and clearing agent and was then infiltrated for 48 hours at 60° C. When series of sections from all three blocks were prepared by the glycerophosphate method, comparison of the sections showed that a loss of about 50 percent of the enzyme had occurred in both the second and third blocks (using the frozen sections as standard); but there was no significant difference between the second and third blocks themselves. Thus extension of the time of fixation, clearing, infiltration, etc., does not appear to increase the amount of destruction of enzyme. In the second series of experiments, large numbers of sections were cut from one block of paraffin-embedded rat kidney. A number of control sections were taken through the whole glycerophosphate procedure as quickly as possible, apart from a period of 1 hour for incubation in the glycerophosphate mixture. The experimental group of sections was taken through all steps in the procedure, bar one, as rapidly as the control sections, but it was exposed to this one step in the procedure for 24 hours; i.e., an experimental section was exposed to, e.g., xylol, alcohol, or collodion, or simply kept at 37° in air after flattening, or in distilled water before incubation, or in calcium nitrate, cobalt nitrate, distilled water, ammonium sulfide, or one of the alcohols or xylols after incubation, for 24 hours. The loss of apparent enzyme activity amounted to 100 percent in some of these steps. Further study was made of those steps which caused loss of apparent enzyme activity. The results are incorporated in Table II which gives both the duration of each step which has been found to be generally convenient in the laboratory and the maximum duration of the steps which I have found caused no loss of enzyme activity. It is probable that some of the steps may be even more protracted than suggested in the table without causing loss of enzyme activity. On the other hand, certain steps, notably k, l, and m, of the table are very likely to cause loss of apparent activity, so that timing of these operations must be very carefully controlled. Although step m (washing in tap water after ammonium sulfide) may cause loss of enzyme activity if protracted, sections may be left for many hours in tap water to which a little ammonium sulfide has been added without loss of apparent activity.

Where small traces of phosphatase activity are being studied, it is advisable to add one drop of 0.1 M disodium phosphate solution to the incubation mixture, and then filter off the precipitate before incubation. This insures that the incubation mixture is saturated in phosphate ion so that any trace of phosphate which is liberated by enzyme activity is more likely to be precipitated. As noted earlier, it is also necessary to add a little sodium veronal to the calcium nitrate, cobalt nitrate, and distilled water which are used after incubation; this is necessary to counteract

TABLE II

Time limits of the various steps in the procedure of Takamatsu and Gomori.

Step in Procedure	Convenient Duration	Maximum Duration Found to Cause No Loss of Activity
Steps before incubation		
(a) Fixation	2 hours	24 hours
(b) Dehydration (3 changes)	6 hours	72 hours
(c) Clearing (3 changes of cedarwood oil)	6–24 hours	72 hours
(d) Infiltration with wax	0.5–24 hours	48 hours
(e) Drying of sections on slide at room temperature in desiccator at 37° C. in incubator	2–24 hours	7 days
(f) Removal of wax in xylol	3 minutes	24 hours
(g) In celloidin or alcohols	1 minute	24 hours
(h) In distilled water	5–60 minutes	24 hours
Steps after incubation		
(i) In calcium nitrate	5 minutes	7 days
(j) In cobalt nitrate	2 minutes	24 hours
(k) In distilled water	1 minute	2 minutes
(l) In ammonium sulfide	1 minute	24 hours
(m) In tap water	5–10 minutes	30 minutes
(n) In alcohols or xylols	3 minutes	5 minutes

any tendency towards acidity in these solutions, which would, of course, cause removal of precipitate from the sections.

Intact paraffin blocks will often keep 12 months or more without serious loss of activity. The enzyme in blocks which have been cut often seems to be less stable.

THE DETECTION OF DIFFUSION ARTEFACTS

We may classify the artefacts which may arise by diffusion processes into three groups.

1. Diffusion of calcium phosphate, cobalt phosphate, or cobalt sulfide.

2. Diffusion of enzyme, enzyme activator, or enzyme inhibitor after fixation.

3. Diffusion of enzyme, enzyme activator, or enzyme inhibitor during fixation.

If the glycerophosphate technique is to have biological significance, one needs to establish that the cobalt sulfide precipitate produced by this technique demonstrates with precision the site of enzyme activity, and also that the enzyme is in its physiologically normal position. This can be best demonstrated by separate consideration of the three groups of diffusion artefacts just mentioned. It should, however, be noted that as yet no studies have been made of the concentrations of activators, inhibitors, substrates, etc., for phosphatase which are found in the immediate vicinity of the enzyme in the living cell. Until such studies are made, even the demonstration of the presence of enzyme in its physiologically normal site does not enable us to foretell with certainty the extent to which the enzyme is in fact active at its site.

SITES OF AFFINITY FOR CALCIUM PHOSPHATE

In the glycerophosphate technique the initial precipitate which is formed is calcium phosphate. It is therefore of interest to determine to what extent fixed material has local sites of special affinity for such substances. The best way to test this is to cause the liberation of phosphate in the incubation mixture by the spontaneous decomposition of a labile ester, and to observe the extent to which the liberated phosphate is precipitated in sections which are devoid of enzyme activity. The phosphatase of tissue sections may readily be inactivated by exposure to wet steam for 10 minutes, or by being placed in water at 90° C. for 2 minutes.

A solution containing a labile ester may be obtained simply by adding hydrogen peroxide to the normal glycerophosphate incubation mixture. The glycerophosphate undergoes oxidation, and phosphate ion is slowly liberated and precipitated by the calcium ions present in the medium. After addition of hydrogen peroxide it is necessary to readjust the pH to 9.3, after which inactive sections may be inserted and incubation carried out at 37° C. Sections of kidney and of healing wounds in rat skin were studied in this manner. The nuclei of the kidney section were found to take up calcium phosphate with much avidity, but the brush borders did not display any significant affinity for calcium phosphate. In sections of healing wounds the nuclei and the newly formed collagen fibres displayed a high affinity for calcium phosphate. In these two types of section, the distribution of phosphatase as demonstrated by the glycerophosphate technique with sections containing active enzyme is such that the brush-border regions of the kidney contain the highest concentrations of phosphatase, newly formed collagen the next highest, and nuclei a moderate to low concentration of phosphatase. It is thus clear that some sites which appear to contain phosphatase have a high affinity for calcium phosphate but that there is no correlation between this affinity and the absolute concentrations of phosphatase appearing in the cells.

THE ABILITY OF CALCIUM PHOSPHATE TO DIFFUSE WITHIN A SECTION

As noted just above, when a tissue section is heated it loses its phosphatase activity, but retains its affinity for calcium phos-

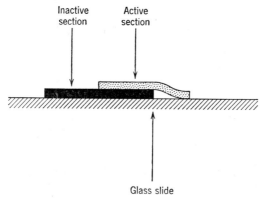

FIG. 2. Illustrating arrangement of active and inactive sections on a slide required to test for diffusion artefacts.

phate. It is therefore possible by superimposing a section containing active enzyme upon a section in which the enzyme has been destroyed to test the extent to which calcium phosphate may diffuse in sections from one site to another. It is best to arrange the sections as illustrated in Fig. 2 with the inert section lying underneath the section containing active enzyme, so as to observe the maximum effect of diffusion of calcium phosphate. In the first studies which were made using this technique (in 1944), active kidney sections were placed upon inactive sections of kidney, spleen, and healing wounds. I found that with 12 hours' incubation there was no evidence for diffusion of calcium phosphate. It is therefore clear that, when the experiment is carried out with the conditions and timing set out here, calcium phosphate does not diffuse during the experimental procedure to a degree that can produce a precipitation which might be interpreted as indicating the presence of enzyme in a position in which it is not intrinsically present. It is also clear, of course, that neither the cobalt phosphate nor the cobalt sulfide can be diffusing to such an extent as to produce an observable artefact. We must therefore conclude that the site of precipitation of calcium phosphate is identical with the site of enzyme activity. It is important in studies of effects of this type that judgment should be based upon diffusion from an active section into an inactive section of the same material. If the underlying section is of a different material from the active section, and evidence for a diffusion artefact should be found, this would not constitute evidence that similar artefacts would occur in the active section, since affinities for various substances differ from one tissue to another.

When, as may occur in some instances, the enzyme itself is diffusible, the technique given above may not make it possible to make an independent study of the extent to which calcium phosphate is diffusing in a section. We may then resort to the device of carrying out the experiment in superimposed sections in the presence of different concentrations of calcium ion in the incubation mixture. Since calcium ion is present in the incubation mixture in a great excess, the rate at which calcium phosphate can be transferred from one site on the section to another site depends upon the solubility of phosphate ion. We have the equation:

$$[Ca^{2+}]^3[PO_4^{3-}]^2 = \text{constant}$$

defining the solubility of phosphate ion, i.e.,

$$[PO_4^{3-}] = \sqrt{\text{Constant}/[Ca^{2+}]^3}$$

Thus we see that the rate at which an artefact can be established due to the diffusion of calcium phosphate will depend upon the calcium ion concentration in the incubation medium.

THE SITE OF LIBERATION OF THE ALCOHOL MOIETY OF
PHOSPHATE ESTERS

Although the evidence from the study of precipitated calcium phosphate appears to show quite clearly that techniques involving the precipitation of calcium phosphate indicate reliably the site of alkaline phosphatase, it nevertheless seemed desirable to reinforce this evidence by attempts to secure a precipitation of the alcohol moiety of the phosphate esters. This would be very difficult to do with glycerophosphate. But with a number of other esters of phosphoric acid it has been found possible to secure the precipitation of the alcohol concerned. The chief substrates which proved useful in this connection are:

1. Phenolphthalein phosphate.
2. β-Naphthol phosphate.
3. p-Nitrophenylazo-α-naphthol phosphate.

When phenolphthalein phosphate is studied, the calcium salt is used in saturated solution in an incubation mixture containing calcium. Under these conditions both moieties of the ester are precipitated, the phosphate moiety as calcium phosphate and the phenolphthalein probably as a calcium salt. After incubation the sections are dried in air until the greater part of the water has evaporated and are then exposed to ammonia vapor. This converts the phenolphthalein into the bright-red alkaline form. If a sufficient amount of water has been removed from the section, phenolphthalein does not diffuse out at a significant rate, and its distribution may be photographed. If, however, too much water is removed by drying, ammonia does not convert the phenolphthalein into the red form. To obtain just the right amount of moisture in the section is a somewhat tricky procedure. When the phenolphthalein distribution has been recorded photographically, the distribution of calcium phosphate may be ascertained by conversion of the calcium phosphate to cobalt sulfide, as in the standard glycerophosphate technique. The section may then again be photographed. It is found by this method that the distribution of phenolphthalein is closely similar to that of calcium phosphate, with the reservation that, as the colour of phenolphthalein is much less intense than that of cobalt sulfide, it is not possible to observe the presence of phenolphthalein in the sites which show a low activity by the calcium phosphate method.

The distribution obtained by this method is closely similar to that obtained by the use of glycerophosphate in the substrate. It might be thought that phenolphthalein has a specific affinity for either certain parts of tissues or for the calcium phosphate which is precipitated. This was shown not to be so by exposing sections to a strong solution of phenolphthalein. There was no specific staining of the section. Also, when to a solution of phenolphthalein in the incubation mixture a little alkaline sodium phosphate solution was added, phenolphthalein is not carried down to a significant extent by the precipitate of calcium phosphate which is formed. These two experiments show quite clearly that the precipitation of phenolphthalein as a result of enzyme activity occurs owing to its insolubility and not by adsorption at sites which have a specific affinity for phenolphthalein.

As mentioned previously, phenol phosphates do not react directly with diazonium hydroxides. Consequently, when a phenol phosphate and a diazonium hydroxide are mixed in alkaline solution, no reaction takes place. But, when a section is placed in this mixture, if alkaline phosphatase is present it splits phenol and phosphate from the ester, and the phenol rapidly reacts with any diazonium hydroxide which is present. Thus by using a suitable diazonium hydroxide and a suitable phenol, it should be possible to secure the precipitation of the phenol released by enzyme action, at the actual site of enzyme action. The most commonly used substances for this purpose are α- or β-naphthol phosphate and diazotised α-naphthylamine, which react as follows:

When mammalian kidney sections are studied by this method, the azo dye is precipitated in the brush borders and also in the nuclei of white cells (Table III). It is usually not found in the nuclei of the other cells present in the tissue. There are probably two reasons why the low concentration of phosphatase in the other cell nuclei cannot be demonstrated by this technique. In the first place, the azo dye is not completely insoluble in water and it is probable that, unless the rate of production of the azo compound at a particular site exceeds a given limit, precipitation does not occur in the section. Secondly, the diazonium hydroxide also reacts with certain components of the tissue section themselves, producing a background stain. Very small amounts of precipitated azo dye cannot be distinguished from the background staining. It may also, of course, be possible that nuclear enzymes react less vigorously with β-napthol phosphate than with glycerophosphate. Provided that the azo dye resulting from the interaction of the phenol and diazonium hydroxide is sufficiently insoluble, the same result is obtained with any mixture of phenol phosphate and diazonium hydroxide. Table III summarises results which have been obtained with a number of different bases.

TABLE III

Summary of results obtained by exposing kidney sections containing active phosphatase to a solution at pH 9.3 containing a phenol phosphate and a diazotised amine. The remarks refer to the localization of dye produced by the interaction of the diazonium hydroxide with a phenol liberated by the action of the enzyme on a phenol phosphate.

Amine Used	Staining of Control	Site of Dye Precipitated with Sodium Naphthol Phosphate	Calcium Naphthol Phosphate
α-Aminonaphthoquinone in saturated solution	Deep	Not localized	Brush borders
p-Nitroaniline, 0.2%	Pale	Not localized	In cortex but not restricted to brush borders
Benzidine, 0.2%	Moderate	Brush borders	Brush borders
α-Naphthylamine	Pale	Brush borders	Brush borders
β-Naphthylamine	Pale	Brush borders	Brush borders

The third substrate, p-nitrophenylazo-α-naphthol phosphate, is itself the phosphate ester of an insoluble dye. The solution of the phosphate ester is probably colloidal. When kidney sections are immersed in a solution of this dye phosphate at pH 9.3, the dye appears both in the brush borders and in the nuclei. However, not all the nuclei are in fact stained in this manner. Of two adjacent nuclei, one may stain and one may not. As was the case when naphthol phosphate was used as a substrate, this is probably due to the necessity for the rate of liberation of dye in a particular site to reach a critical level before precipitation can occur. In those nuclei which have a concentration of enzyme high enough for this critical rate of liberation to be reached, precipitation occurs. In those nuclei in which the critical rate is not reached, no precipitation occurs. The same phenomena can also be observed with this substrate in the brush borders themselves. Some regions of the brush borders contain a rather low level of phosphatase activity and do not stain at all with this substrate, whereas most of the brush-border region has a high concentration of phosphatase and is deeply stained by the substrate.

When we consider the results of studying the precipitation of both the phosphate moiety and the alcoholic moiety of a phosphate ester after liberation by enzyme action, it seems impossible to escape the conclusion that in all cases, within the limits defined by the study of diffusion artefacts, the precipitate produced is in fact at the site of enzyme activity. If this were not so, the same region of tissues would need to have an affinity for calcium phosphate, phenolphthalein, and various azo dyes. Kidney tissue has no affinity for any of the azo dyes or for phenolphthalein. Calcium phosphate has an affinity for one of the two main sites of activity in kidney sections but, on the other hand, has been shown to be unable to diffuse within a section to a significant degree. It is thus certain that the site of alkaline phosphatase in tissue sections is truly demonstrated by these cytochemical methods.

THE EFFECT OF THICKNESS OF THE SECTION

All the various procedures which have been outlined above in connection with different techniques were worked out for sections between 5 and 8 μ in thickness. It is sometimes necessary to use sections which are thicker or thinner than this. When this is done, it may be necessary to consider whether any of the times of the various treatments should be modified. Obviously a time of washing which may be satisfactory for a 2 μ section may not be satisfactory for a 16 μ section. Whether this is so depends on whether the major resistance to diffusion is encountered in diffusing out of or into the tissue section, or whether the dead layer of water surrounding the section constitutes the major barrier. If the resistance to diffusion is a function of the thickness of the section, then the time required to secure a given degree of washing should be roughly proportional to the square root of the thickness, whereas, if the dead layer of the water is the main factor, the time for obtaining this given degree of washing should be independent of the thickness. To investigate this point a number of series of sections were cut at 1 μ, 2 μ, 4 μ, 8 μ, and 16 μ. These were incubated in the glycerophosphate incubation mixture for 15 minutes, and then developed with the usual cobalt technique, with the exception that different sections of the same thickness were washed for various lengths of time in distilled water. The times for washing varied between 0.25 minute and 16 minutes. Owing to the solubility of cobalt phosphate in distilled water, washing for more than 2 minutes with an 8 μ section causes loss of apparent enzyme activity from a section if carried out in distilled water. The losses are much smaller if the washing is carried out in 0.002 percent sodium veronal, as was the case with the results displayed in Table IV. Under such conditions the minimum washing time for removal of cobalt nitrate increases from about 1 minute for 1 μ sections to about 4 minutes for 16 μ sections; with 1 μ sections a significant amount of cobalt phosphate was not removed from the section even after 16 minutes' washing.

It may perhaps be mentioned here that, whereas most tissues do not take up cobalt to a significant degree from cobalt nitrate solution, this is not the case when ova are studied. The yolk of echinoderm ova, for example, takes up cobalt very readily: this cobalt cannot be removed by washing in distilled water without also removing any cobalt phosphate which is present. So far no satisfactory solution has been found to this problem, but it seems possible that, if a lead or copper solution is sub-

TABLE IV

The effect of washing sections of various thicknesses for various lengths of time. The sections were of rat kidney incubated with glycerophosphate by the Gomori method, after which calcium phosphate present in the section was converted into cobalt phosphate by treatment with cobalt nitrate. The sections were then washed in 0.002 percent sodium veronal. + indicates that the section is washed free of cobalt nitrate but has lost no appreciable amount of cobalt phosphate.

Section Thickness in Microns	Washing Time in Minutes					
	0.25	1	2	4	8	16
1		+	+	+	+	+
2		+	+	+	+	+
4			+	+	+	+
8			+	+	+	+
16				+	+	+

stituted for the cobalt solution, and the sections are washed in dilute acetic acid or citric acid instead of in distilled water, the yolk could be freed from stain without dissolving the precipitated phosphate.

The Physiological Sites of Phosphatase Activity

It has been demonstrated that the various cytochemical reactions do indicate sites of alkaline phosphatase in the section. It still remains to be shown that the enzyme in a fixed preparation does not diffuse to a significant degree during or after fixation. Neumann has demonstrated that practically all the phosphatase may be removed from some materials by prolonged contact with 30 percent alcohol. Clearly, exposure to dilute alcohol must be avoided if diffusion of phosphatase is not to cause serious difficulty. So far as I am aware, Martin and Jacoby (1949) were the first to obtain clear evidence that phosphatase may diffuse during the course of incubation. There are at least three possible methods of estimating the extent to which the distribution of phosphatase is modified by diffusion. In all these methods it is necessary to use a logarithmic series of incubation times. The exact lengths of time of incubation must be chosen according to the amount of phosphatase which is present in the section.

The first method is to use superimposed sections, as was done in the study of the diffusion of calcium phosphate recorded above. This method of using superimposed sections will, in fact, in one operation record the diffusion, if any, of phosphatase, calcium phosphate, cobalt phosphate, and cobalt sulfide. A detailed example of the use of this method will be given later when the occurrence of phosphatase in cell nuclei is discussed.

The method of using superimposed sections is quite convenient when the tissue components which are to be studied constitute a considerable fraction of the area of the section. But when the tissue component constitutes only a small fraction of the section, it is difficult to superimpose a section containing active enzyme upon a section containing no enzyme in such a manner as to obtain an active tissue component immediately above the corresponding inactive component in the underlying section. Under these circumstances, both loss of time and waste of material may be avoided by using series of sections which have been incubated for the usual logarithmic series of times in a number of dilutions of the same substrate. As the substrate concentration is diminished the rate of enzyme action is also diminished, and, consequently, the rate at which a given component attains a given degree of staining is diminished. On the other hand, the rate of development of diffusion artefacts due to diffusion of phosphatase will not be seriously affected by changing the substrate concentration. Consequently, by comparing the series of slides which have been incubated in the different substrate concentrations, it is possible to determine the extent to which phosphatase is diffusing within the section.

As an alternative to various concentrations of the same substrate, a given concentration of different substrates may be studied, the same logarithmic series of times of incubation being used. If the substrates are split by the enzyme at different rates, comparison of the series incubated in the various substrates should again demonstrate the extent of diffusion of phosphatase.

So far I have not made use of this last method. We are at present studying the use of phenol phosphate and paranitrophenyl phosphate to see whether these compounds together with glycerophosphate constitute a satisfactory series. The rate at which phosphate is split from these esters by ordinary alkaline hydrolysis varies about a hundredfold or more.

In the various studies which I have made, artefacts due to the diffusion of phosphatase have usually not occurred within the time period of incubation which was necessary to obtain adequate information about the distribution of enzyme within sections. In the few cases where diffusion has occurred to a significant degree, the methods indicated above have made it quite simple to assess its importance, with one exception. The exceptional case is that of tissue cultures, which will be discussed later.

Martin and Jacoby, in a study of the distribution of phosphatase in the small intestine, appear to have encountered very much greater difficulty with diffusion of phosphatase: this is no doubt due to the fact that the small intestine usually contains a considerable concentration of diffusible phosphatase which acts as a digestive enzyme. They appear to have had difficulty also in interpreting their results with other tissues: this seems in part due to incubation for an excessive length of time. But there are also two points in their experimental procedure which may have caused them some difficulty. In the first place, many of their experiments involved superimposing tissue sections on sections of different material, usually guinea-pig liver. Now it is of no interest to know to what extent enzymes will diffuse from one tissue into another. What is important is to know to what extent enzymes will diffuse *within* a tissue and thus give rise to artefacts. It is therefore essential that experiments with superimposed sections should be carried out with an active section superimposed on an inert section of the same material. The second fault in their procedure lay in rinsing the sections in distilled water immediately after incubation. The section at this stage contains precipitated calcium phosphate which has a very significant solubility in water in the absence of calcium ions, or if the pH is shifted much below pH 9. The effect of rinsing in distilled water is to shift the pH towards the acid side and at the same time to diminish the calcium ion concentration. It is thus possible that the precipitate of calcium phosphate formed in their sections was partially dissolved by rinsing in distilled water when, of course, it would be freely diffusible. Subsequently, when they transferred the sections from distilled water to cobalt nitrate solution, reprecipitation would occur at many cites, and simulate diffusion artefacts.

DIFFUSION OF ENZYME DURING FIXATION

We have seen that the position of an enzyme within a section may be determined with some accuracy and that the extent to which the enzyme diffuses within a section may also be determined without difficulty. It remains to be seen whether the enzyme present in a fixed preparation is in its physiologically normal position.

As was indicated in the chapter on fixation, the only method of fixation which is sufficiently rapid to exclude diffusion of an enzyme is freeze-drying. Where this method is used, one may be sure that diffusion of phosphatase does not occur during fixation. Where freeze-drying cannot be used, the extent of diffusion, and the site at which the diffused enzyme appears, can in some cases be detected, provided that a wide variety of fixatives are used. With a variety of fixatives the time available for diffusion and the adsorption conditions prevailing in the specimen should vary considerably from fixative to fixative.

In a study of the action of chemical fixatives, a number of individual components of fixatives were tested for their direct action upon the enzyme by placing a section from an alcohol-fixed block in the fixative component. After 2 hours' exposure to the fixative component the sections were washed carefully and then incubated for the same length of time as control sections. The fixative components tested in this way were 8 percent formaldehyde; saturated picric acid; saturated magnesium sulfate; saturated ammonium sulfate; saturated calcium chloride; saturated mercuric chloride; 1 percent, 5 percent, 10 percent, and 50 percent acetic acid; 1 percent trichloroacetic acid; 10 percent pyridine; acetone; chloroform; dry pyridine, alcoholic iodine, 1 percent osmic acid; 1 percent iodine in potassium iodide; 0.04 percent reduced thioglycollate; 0.04 percent reduced glutathione; and 0.04 percent oxidized glutathione. Phosphatase was completely destroyed by mercury, osmic acid, trichloroacetic acid, iodine, and concentrations of acetic acid higher than 1 percent. There was a marked reduction in the amount of enzyme activity caused by formaldehyde, magnesium sulfate, ammonium sulfate, picric acid, and reduced thiols, but the amount of reduction in activity was not sufficient to preclude their use in fixatives.

TABLE V

Distribution of alkaline phosphatase in sections after fixation in various media, and after freeze-drying. $++$ indicates gross shrinkage; $+$, some shrinkage; 0, no change; —, some swelling; $=$, gross swelling.

Fixative	Shrinkage	Fixation	Distribution of Enzyme
None	0	....	Mainly in cortical tubules: smeared appearance
Freeze-drying	0	Excellent	Brush borders and nuclei
Ethyl alcohol 80%	$+$	Fair	Brush borders and nuclei
Formaldehyde 4% + sodium chloride 1%	0	Good	Brush borders and nuclei
Acetone	$+$	Fair	Brush borders and nuclei
Pyridine	$+$	Good	Brush borders and nuclei
Pyridine 70%	$+$	Good	Brush borders and nuclei
Pyridine 25% in alcohol 80%	0	Good	Brush borders and nuclei
Calcium chloride 1% in pyridine 70%	$+$	Good	Brush borders and nuclei
Formaldehyde 4% + calcium chloride 1%	$+$	Good	Brush borders and nuclei
Saturated picric + formaldehyde 4%	0	Fair	Enzyme destroyed
Ethyl alcohol 65% + chloroform 35%	0	Poor	Enzyme spread all over proximal tubules
Pyridine 70% + formaldehyde 4%	$=$	Very poor	Enzyme spread over whole section
Pyridine 20% + ethyl alcohol 70% + formaldehyde 4%	0	Very good	Brush borders and nuclei
Alcohol 60% + chloroform 30% + formaldehyde 4%	0	Poor	Brush borders and nuclei; some spreading into cytoplasm
Formaldehyde 4% + acetic acid 1%	—	Very good	Brush borders and nuclei
Formaldehyde 4% + acetic acid 5%	0	Good	Enzyme destroyed
Ethyl alcohol 80% + acetic acid 1%	$=$	Fair	Brush borders and nuclei
Pyridine 25% + picric (sat. soln.) 75%	0	Fair	Brush borders and nuclei
Saturated aqueous ammonium sulfate followed by alcohol 80%	$+$	Fair	Brush borders and nuclei
Saturated aqueous calcium chloride followed by alcohol 80%	$++$	Poor	Brush borders and nuclei
Saturated aqueous magnesium sulfate followed by alcohol 80%	$++$	Fair	Brush borders and nuclei

Consequently, a series of fixatives were made up as indicated in Table V. Into these fixatives were placed pieces of rat kidney approximately 1 millimeter thick. The fixative was allowed to act for 2 hours, after which the tissue was washed in water, frozen sections were prepared, and the sections were incubated for logarithmic series of times for each fixative. As will be seen in the table, where the fixation was generally satisfactory from a cytological point of view the enzyme in kidney tissue was restricted to the brush-border region and to the nuclei. This conclusion was reinvestigated later with the freeze-drying method. On the whole, the general nature of the conclusions reached with chemical fixatives was confirmed. But it was also found that with all the chemical fixatives some diffusion of phosphatase into the nuclei appeared to occur. With chemical fixation the chromocentres of the nuclei appeared to contain much more phosphatase than in freeze-dried specimens. Thus in the case of kidney tissue the broad outline of the results obtained with chemical fixatives is correct, but the detailed distribution of phosphatase cannot be studied without freeze-drying. In all the tissues which I have studied all the cytologically satisfactory fixatives give a picture substantially similar to that obtained by freeze-drying. This, however, may not be the case with tissues containing large amounts of freely diffusible phosphatase, such as small intestine.

The general conclusion appears to be that freeze-drying should be employed wherever possible. Where this is impossible, a wide variety of fixing agents will probably give an overall picture which is correct in outline but misleading in detail.

The General Status of Techniques for the Localization of Alkaline Phosphatase

The general conclusions which may be drawn from critical studies of alkaline phosphatase techniques differ slightly with the various techniques. In all cases it is desirable, as indicated above, to use methods for the detection of diffusion artefacts based upon the technique of imposed sections, or one of the other techniques given above. When this is done, where the initial precipitate is calcium phosphate, fairly accurate localization of enzyme can be determined even within a nucleus, though it is quite possible, for example, that the detailed distribution of phosphatase on the chromosomes is not an accurate representation of the enzyme distribution *in vivo*. With the techniques involving azo dyes, less accuracy is possible. It is quite possible to say whether the nucleus of a mammalian somatic cell has phosphatase or not. But it is not possible with the azo-dye techniques to determine the details of the distribution of phosphatase within a given nucleus of this size. Neumann, and Martin and Jacoby, have expressed considerable pessimism about some of these techniques. This pessimism, however, is based partly upon results obtained with techniques which to me appear to be defective in certain essentials, and particularly upon failure to use adequate methods of studying diffusion artefacts, so as to make a quantitative estimate of the extent of diffusion.

Alkaline Phosphatases of Cell Nuclei

Studies have been made by many investigators on mass preparations of cell nuclei prepared by various methods. However, as was pointed out in the first chapter of this book, there are two major difficulties which make it impossible at the present time to evaluate studies on mass preparations of cell components prepared by maceration techniques. These difficulties are that substances diffuse in and out of nuclei fairly readily when nuclei are suspended in aqueous solutions, and that in addition to this the nuclei prepared from most organs cannot consist completely of nuclei from one cell type only. In view of these difficulties, the only method which at present can provide reliable information as to whether there is alkaline phosphatase in cell nuclei is the cytochemical method. A typical result is that obtained with rat kidney, shown in Plate IV, Fig. *A*. There is a certain amount of phosphatase in the nuclei of the kidney tubule cells, particularly in the nuclei of the cells of the proximal tubules. There is a very much greater amount of phosphatase present in the brush border of the proximal tubule cells. It is clearly quite possible that the phosphatase in the nuclei may not be intrinsic phosphatase of the nuclei, but may have reached the nuclei by diffusion from the brush-border regions. It is, therefore, necessary to examine this material by the superimposed-section technique described earlier in this chapter (p. 37). Plate IV shows some of the results obtained when kidney sections containing active enzyme were superimposed upon kidney sections in which the enzyme had been inactivated. The sections were incubated for periods as follows: 5, 10, 20, 40, 80, 160, 320, 640, and 1280 minutes. Plate IV, Fig. B, shows that the nuclei of the proximal tubules in the section containing active enzymes are positive for phosphatase in the case of the rat kidney after only 5 minutes' incubation. Guinea-pig kidney in our experience has usually required 10 minutes' incubation to demonstrate the intrinsic phosphatase. At this time no phosphatase has appeared in the inactivated underlying section. Plate IV, Fig. C, shows the result obtained after 320 minutes' incubation with the rat kidney. The section containing active enzymes has produced so vigorous a reaction for phosphatase that it is no longer possible to see all the detail of distribution of the enzyme. The underlying section is still devoid of phosphatase activity. Plate IV, Fig. D, shows the result obtained in the underlying inert section after 640 minutes' incubation. The amount of phosphatase which is demonstrated in the inert section is comparable with that found in the section containing active enzyme after only 4 or 5 minutes' incubation. When kidneys from different animals are studied in this way, there is some variation in the time at which evidence of diffusion of phosphatase is manifest. Sometimes in the guinea-pig kidney phosphatase may appear in the underlying section after only 320 minutes' incubation. The amount of phosphatase which may have diffused into the underlying section after a lengthy period of incubation (1280 minutes) is considerable. With the material which we have investigated, we have never found any considerable amount of diffusible phosphatase in rat kidney revealed with incubations of 320 minutes or less. But sometimes, after 1280 minutes' incubation with guinea-pig kidney, there may be a very heavy reaction in the underlying section. This reaction, of course, is entirely due to diffusion artefacts.

It is clear from these results that the phosphatase which is seen in the nuclei of kidney after periods of incubation up to 160 minutes is intrinsic phosphatase. After twice this period it is possible that part of the reaction observed is due to diffusion artefacts. But the amount of phosphatase which may have diffused into the nuclei by this time is less than 5 percent of the phosphatase which was intrinsically present in the nuclei. After longer periods of incubation the amount of phosphatase which may be present in the nuclei as a result of diffusion may, of course, be much greater, so that the magnitude of the diffusion artefact becomes increasingly serious. However, all the detail of the distribution of phosphatase in mammalian kidney is readily observed after only 10 or 20 minutes' incubation, so that in this material there is no difficulty in eliminating diffusion artefacts, so far as the distribution of alkaline phosphatase is concerned.

The experiment mentioned above, however, shows quite clearly that, where protracted incubations are carried out with material which contains a rich source of phosphatase, the diffusion artefact may become quite serious. Plate V, Fig. *A*, is a low-power view of a liver section which was devoid of enzyme activity, superimposed upon which was a guinea-pig kidney section containing active enzyme. These sections were incubated for 1280 minutes. It will be seen that the enzyme has spread from the active section to a distance equal to more than seven cell diameters of the kidney section. Some tissues, such as the small intestine, when under normal physiological conditions contain active diffusible phosphatase. It seems very probable that with such tissues diffusion artefacts may be much more serious. The work of Martin and Jacoby has, indeed, provided some evidence that this is the case.

I have made a few experiments to try to ascertain the nature of the substance diffusing from an active kidney section which leads to the apparent appearance of phosphatase activity in the underlying inactive section. The substances most likely to be diffusing were calcium phosphate, alkaline phosphatase itself, or an activator for phosphatase. As was indicated on p. 38, if the diffusing substance is calcium phosphate, the rate of appearance of the artefact should be a function of the calcium concentration. However, when the Gomori-Takamatsu method for alkaline phosphatase was carried out in the presence of calcium concentrations 10 times greater than, or only $\frac{1}{10}$, that of the normal, no significant difference was observed in the rate of appearance of the diffusion artefact. Had the diffusing substance been calcium phosphate, the rate of appearance of the artefact should have varied about a hundredfold with this variation in the calcium concentration. It is, therefore, clear that the diffusing material is not calcium phosphate.

The next test was to ascertain whether the diffusing substance might be alkaline phosphatase itself or an activator for alkaline phosphatase. In these experiments the underlying sections were either kidney sections or guinea-pig liver sections in which the phosphatase activity had been destroyed by heating, by dipping in hot water, or by exposure to dilute acid. Superimposed upon the inactivated section was a 50 μ section of guinea-pig kidney. The top section was allowed to remain in contact with the underlying section for 2 days in a sodium barbitone-calcium nitrate solution (corresponding to the incubation medium but without substrate for phosphatase). After that period the superimposed section was removed and the underlying section incubated by itself. Plate V, Fig. *B*, shows the result obtained. There is an intense reaction for phosphatase in what was originally material lacking phosphatase. Since the *active* section was removed before any incubation in the presence of substrate for phosphatase was carried out, it follows that the diffusing substance cannot be calcium phosphate, cobalt phosphate, or cobalt sulfide. It must be either phosphatase itself or a substance present in the active section which can activate phosphatase in an underlying section.

So far it has not been possible to discover whether the diffusing substance is phosphatase or activator. If a layer of collodium or cellophane is inserted between the inactive section and the active one, the amount of diffusion is reduced to zero. But this experiment does not decisively distinguish between the two possibilities.

When diffusion occurs from an active section into a liver section, the pattern of distribution of the diffused material is considerably different from that of the intrinsic phosphatase of the liver section. Plate V, Fig. *C*, shows the phosphatase which is intrinsically present in a guinea-pig liver section. It is mainly present in the cell nuclei. Figure *B* of Plate V, on the other hand, shows that when diffusion occurs the nuclei are only one of the sites which take up the phosphatase reaction. It thus seems probable that, unless guinea-pig liver contains a considerable amount of an apoenzyme, which is not normally active when the phosphatase reaction is carried out but which can be activated by an activator which can diffuse from kidney sections, the diffusing substance must be alkaline phosphatase itself.

Investigators who are not familiar with diffusion phenomena may perhaps not be entirely convinced by the arguments given above that the phosphatase of the nuclei of kidney cells is intrinsic phosphatase. We were fortunate in obtaining quite independent evidence that there is intrinsic phosphatase in cell nuclei by the use of another substrate. This is

$$NO_2 \langle \bigcirc \rangle N{=}N \langle \bigcirc \rangle OPO_3H_2$$

which was prepared in an investigation with Dr. A. Loveless. This substance is the phosphate of a dye, which gave a reddish-yellow solution. Our first preparations of this material were purified rather carefully and, to our surprise, were not readily hydrolyzed by alkaline phosphatase. A preparation by a different route, which was not highly purified, on the other hand, was readily hydrolyzed by alkaline phosphatase. When kidney sections were incubated in the solution of this impure ester, there was a heavy deposit of red dye in the brush borders and the nuclei of the sections, Plate VI, Fig. A. The dye is precipitated because the free dye is much less soluble in water than is the ester with phosphoric acid. We then set out to investigate why it was that the more highly purified material did not give a phosphatase reaction. It was quickly found that, when a little of the products of hydrolysis of the dye phosphate were added to purified dye phosphate, the purified material was readily split by the enzyme. The split products which were able to facilitate the display of enzyme activity were, of course, phosphate ion and free phenol. By chance, we discovered that the enzyme present in the nuclei was more readily activated by free phenol, whereas the enzyme present in the brush borders was more readily activated by phosphate. When a kidney section was equilibrated with purified dye phosphatase to which a trace of free phenol had been added, we were sometimes able to obtain a reaction in the nuclei only.

Figure *B* of Plate VI shows such a section. The dye material appears only in the nuclei of the cells. As in this experiment the brush-border enzyme was inert, it follows that the nuclear enzyme is intrinsic in the nuclei.

In obtaining such distinction in activity between nuclear and brush-border phosphatases, we were, of course, fortunate to a degree which we cannot expect to see repeated with other tissues. We have also obtained evidence, by destroying enzymes by heat, that nuclear phosphatase is less readily destroyed than is brush-border phosphatase of rat kidney. There thus appear to be two differences between the alkaline phosphatases in rat-kidney nuclei and rat-kidney brush borders. It does not, however, necessarily follow that the enzymes in these two sites are different. It may be that the enzymes in these two sites are adsorbed upon different materials: this might just possibly be sufficient to account for the difference in behaviour.

THE PHOSPHATASES OF THE NUCLEI OF OTHER CELLS

The work mentioned above dealt only with the alkaline phosphatase of the brush-border cells of the proximal tubules of mammalian kidney. In the papers of Takamatsu and Gomori published in 1939 it was mentioned that phosphase is rather commonly demonstrated in a variety of nuclei. Willmer and Krugelis independently showed in 1942, in a study of tissue cultures, that in mitosis the greater part of the nuclear phosphatase becomes concentrated on the chromosomes. From these results it was evident that phosphatase might be playing an important role in some of the chemical activities of the nucleus.

The tendency for phosphatase to become concentrated on the chromosomes during cell division seems to be a fairly common phenomenon. It may be noted, for example, in regenerating liver cells, in tumor cells, and in various embryonic tissues. Plate VII, Fig. *A*, shows phosphatase present in a normal rat liver. The main sites of activity in the nucleolus and the chromocentres are clearly demonstrated. Figure *B* in the same plate shows that when a liver is regenerating, the nuclear phosphatase is concentrated on the chromosomes during the nuclear-division phase. This type of behaviour, i.e., the presence of alkaline phosphatase on chromosomes, nucleoli, and chromocentres, is not limited to mammalian tissues. It has been found in amphibia (Danielli, unpublished) and fish tissues (Lorch, 1949), in various invertebrate tissues (de Nicola, 1949; Danielli, 1950b), and Mugard (1953) has found that in various Protozoa phosphatase is a common nuclear constituent. The nuclear phosphatase of Protozoa is often distributed in a manner similar to the distribution of deoxyribose nucleic acid, as demonstrated by the Feulgen reaction, but undergoes considerable quantitative changes during the various phases of the life history of the Protozoa concerned.

Alkaline phosphatase is also commonly found in tumors. Plate VII, Fig. D, shows the distribution of phosphatase in a section of Walker rat sarcoma. Here again the distribution of alkaline phosphatase tends to follow that of the Feulgen positive material on the chromosomes but differs from the Feulgen positive material in being present in very high concentration in the nucleolus.

When tumor tissues are treated with mitotic poisons, there is again a general tendency for the Feulgen reaction and for the distribution of phosphatase to be similar, except so far as the nucleolus is concerned. Plate VIII shows in Fig. A the distribution of Feulgen-positive material and in Fig. B the distribution of alkaline phosphatase, in both cases in cells in which the mitotic poison has prevented spindle formation, so that when the nuclear membrane broke down the metaphase chromosomes have been distributed throughout the cell. This abnormal behaviour of the chromosomes is frequently followed by pycnotic degeneration, and often at this stage there is a marked parallelism between the Feulgen reaction and the phosphatase distribution, as may be seen from Figs. C and D on the same plate.

The marked tendency for alkaline phosphatase to follow the distribution of Feulgen-positive material can hardly be devoid of significance. Although the occurrence of alkaline phosphatase in the nucleolus is an exception to this general rule, it must be remembered that the nucleolus is a site of high concentration of pentose nucleic acid. Interest in this parallelism has led Danielli and Catcheside in 1945 and Krugelis in 1945 to study the distribution of alkaline phosphatase on the polytene chromosomes of Drosophila salivary gland nuclei. When salivary glands are sectioned after fixation with alcohol, it is easy to demonstrate that the nuclei contain considerable amounts of alkaline phosphatase, and that by far the greater part of this is distributed in bands on the chromosomes. It is difficult, however, to study the detail of the arrangement of the bands in the sectioned material since the nuclei are so packed by the chromosomes. When the material is prepared by the standard procedure of the cytologist, i.e., squashing in 45 percent acetic acid, the phosphatase activity is completely destroyed by the acetic acid. If, on the other hand, the nuclei are fixed by fixatives which have comparatively little action on alkaline phosphatase, such as 80 percent alcohol or aqueous formaldehyde, the nuclei take on a rubbery consistency and cannot be squashed. Thus it appears that fixatives which will give a cytologically satisfactory specimen destroy the enzyme, and fixatives which do not destroy the enzyme do not give a satisfactory cytological preparation. It was, therefore, necessary to compromise between the irreconcilable ideals of good fixation and retention of phosphatase activity by using various concentrations of acetic acid for the preparation of squashes. The best results obtained so far were with squashes prepared in 3.4 percent acetic acid. The procedure of squashing was carried out as rapidly as possible, and immediately after squashing the cover slips were removed under 95 percent alcohol. After the cover slip was removed, the material was left in 95 percent alcohol for at least 30 minutes. Under these conditions most of the material remained on the cover slip, and most of the material was also either cytologically poor or had its alkaline phosphatase destroyed. In occasional specimens, however, moderately well-fixed chromosomes were observed which had a high phosphatase activity. An example of this is shown in Figs. A and B of Plate IX. Catcheside and Danielli found that in the X chromosome it appeared that the type of distribution of phosphatase was identical with that of the Feulgen-positive material. The intensity of the phosphatase reaction in the different bands did not appear to follow the intensity of the Feulgen reaction in the same bands.

The parallelism between the distribution of phosphatase and of what is presumed to be deoxypentose nucleic acid in the known sites of genes has naturally led to the suggestion that both of these substances may be integral parts of genes. An extension of this contention has been the suggestion that a gene may be a specific array of enzyme molecules, whose synthetic

activity is partly defined by the nature of the enzyme molecules present, and partly by the spatial orientation of the
enzymes.

It must be borne in mind that it is not always possible to
demonstrate the presence of alkaline phosphatase in nuclei.
Some of the cells of some organisms may, when examined by
the techniques given above, be lacking in phosphatase either
at some point in their life history, as is often the case with the
Protozoa, or even throughout their life history, so far as information is available at present. But it must be remembered
that none of the cytochemical methods available at present
for the demonstration of alkaline phosphatase are as sensitive
as could be desired, and that failure to demonstrate the presence of phosphatase in a particular site does not mean that
it is absent from that site, but merely that activity cannot be
detected by the cytochemical technique. Thus, as a general
rule, no alkaline phosphatase is observed by the technique of
Gomori in red blood cells. Nevertheless this enzyme may be
readily detectible in red blood cells by biochemical techniques.

Although it is true that phosphatase has not been demonstrated in the nuclei of all tissues, it is, nevertheless, true that
its occurrence is so common, and its distribution so striking,
that, had a cytochemical method for the demonstration of alkaline phosphatase preceded the discovery of the Feulgen
reaction, a large part of the literature on cell nuclei would almost
certainly have been written in terms of the distribution of this
enzyme.

If, however, there is a general significance to be attached to
nuclear alkaline phosphatase of the same magnitude of importance as that to be attached to the Feulgen-positive material, it
should also be possible to demonstrate alkaline phosphatase in
the nuclei of plant cells. My first efforts to demonstrate this
were a complete failure. No doubt many other workers have attempted to find alkaline phosphatase in plant-tissue nuclei by
cytochemical procedures but, as is the case with so many negative results, have not recorded the fact in the literature. However, after some time I discovered (accidentally) that unlike
the alkaline phosphatase of most animal cells, the nuclear phosphatase of plant tissues, or at least of those plant tissues which
I have studied, is rather rapidly destroyed by alcohol. A few

minutes' exposure to 95 percent alcohol causes the destruction of practically the whole of the phosphatase of the nuclei of onion and bean root tips. By working rapidly, however, it has been possible to squash root tips in 80 percent alcohol, remove the cover slip immediately under 95 percent alcohol, allow up to 30 seconds for fixation in the 95 percent alcohol, and then, after removal to distilled water, find some phosphatase still present in the nuclei. For the demonstration of alkaline phosphatase in plant nuclei three methods have been successful: the method of Takamatsu and Gomori, using glycerophosphate as substrate; the use of β-naphthol phosphate as a substrate; and the use of the dye phosphate of Loveless and Danielli as a substrate. Plate X, Fig. A, shows an onion root tip, with glycerophosphate as substrate; Fig. B shows the distribution of phosphatase in an onion root tip, with β-naphthol phosphate as substrate.

It is clear that, whereas the physical properties of the enzyme found in plant tissues and plant-tissue nuclei may differ considerably from those of the animal enzyme, this enzyme is, nevertheless, found in plant nuclei, and that it therefore may well have as general a significance in nuclear processes as has deoxypentose nucleic acid.

The Details of the Distribution of Alkaline Phosphatase in Nuclei

Considerable caution must be exercised in the interpretation of the detailed distribution of phosphatase in cell nuclei, particularly when the nuclei are small, or as far as the finer details are concerned. When one is concerned with large structures such as the bands of *Drosophila* chromosomes, or with the distinction between chromosomes and nucleoli, the method for the detection of diffusion artefacts given earlier in this chapter is quite adequate. I am by no means convinced that it is possible to interpret the detailed picture of apparent phosphatase distribution found with the individual chromosomes of normal somatic tissues, even when full use is made of the critical methods at present available.

When the methods of analysis of the extent to which diffusion artefacts are present cannot be used, interpretation becomes much more hazardous. This is the case, for example, in tissue cultures. Figures *A* to *D* of Plate XI show the distribution of alkaline phosphatase obtained by the method of Takamatsu and Gomori with chick osteoblast cultures. This work on tissue-culture material shows a high concentration of phosphatase in the nuclei. In the intermitotic nuclei by far the highest concentration of phosphatase is found in the nucleolus: the chromocentres are also positive for phosphatase. In early prophase the greater part of the chromosome is positive for phosphatase, even before the nucleoli have disappeared. When the nuclear membrane breaks down and the spindle is formed, the chromosomes retain practically the whole of the alkaline phosphatase activity of the nuclei, but some activity appears on the spindles and particularly on the centrosomes of the spindles. The cytoplasm also commonly shows a certain amount of phosphatase which appears to be present in rather large cytoplasmic granules.

The pictures observed with tissue cultures are often so clear-cut that it is tempting to take them at their face value. But it has not so far been possible to study the extent to which the results are complicated by diffusion artefacts. It is clear that the highest centres of phosphatase activity in the tissue cultures, namely, the nucleoli of intermitotic cells and the chromosomes of mitotic cells, have a high intrinsic phosphatase activity. But whether the phosphatase of the chromocentres, of the spindles, and of the cytoplasmic granules is intrinsic or is in part or wholly due to diffusion artefacts is at present in doubt.

It would, of course, be of the greatest interest if it could be established that there is indeed alkaline phosphatase present in the spindles and in the centrosomes. In sectioned material it is usually not possible to demonstrate alkaline phosphatase in these sites, but I have occasionally found it on the spindle and centrosomes in rat tumor tissues. Further investigation of this problem will be of great interest.

POSSIBLE FUNCTIONS OF NUCLEAR PHOSPHATASE

Until recently alkaline phosphatase was thought of as an enzyme which was apparently hydrolytic in function, producing phosphoric acid and alcohol from a phosphate ester. Axelrod and Meyerhoff and Green have independently demonstrated in the last few years that phosphatases may also act as phosphokinases, i.e., they may catalyze the transfer of a phosphate residue from one organic molecule to another. In considering the possible functions of phosphatase in cell nuclei, we must bear in mind both of these activities of alkaline phosphatase. It must also be borne in mind that the results obtained with *Drosophila* salivary chromosomes indicate that alkaline phosphatase is found associated with all the genes, or at least with a very large number of quite diverse genes, so that its activity cannot be restricted to any very specific function.

If we consider the hydrolytic function of alkaline phosphatase there are at least three possible functions for phosphatase in nuclei. These are:

1. A protective function. An active cell contains a number of vigorous phosphorylating agents such as adenosine triphosphate and acetylphosphate. Exposure of the genes to any of these substances might well be hazardous, and it may be that the function of the alkaline phosphatase of the chromosomes is to protect the genes against the action of these phosphorylating agents.

2. A final stage in synthesis of a gene product may normally be dephosphorylation. For example, if we are to regard the typical gene products as proteins, we must remember that it is quite possible that protein synthesis involves the formation of a phospho-protein, and that the action of alkaline phosphatase in the nuclei is to split off the phosphate residue from the protein, and thus liberate an active product from an inactive precursor. It is of interest to reflect that the occurrence of phospho-proteins in milk and in the yolk of eggs need not necessarily denote a special synthesis of a phospho-protein in these instances. It may instead be an indication of the suspension of a dephosphorylation process, which is normally carried out when the function of the nucleus is to pass an active protein into the cytoplasm. That is, by the suspension of dephosphorylation, it may be that proteins which would otherwise participate in the chemical reactions proceeding in cytoplasm are protected against such activity and thus can be stored.

3. A third possibility is that alkaline phosphatase is concerned in some way with nucleic acid synthesis. Such a proposal has been made by several authors. It is, however, far from clear in what way alkaline phosphatase might be concerned.

If we consider alkaline phosphatase as a phosphokinase, there are at least two possibilities involved. The first of these is that synthesis of phosphate esters may be a normal function of the nucleus, and that the function of alkaline phosphatase is to transfer phosphate groups from precursor substances to the specific molecules which are involved in the activities of genes. An alternative function is that alkaline phosphatase might serve as a phosphokinase in the conservation of phosphate bond energy. If gene products must be dephosphorylated to release the product of the gene in active form, a considerable economy of the energy of the phosphate bond would be effected if, instead of hydrolyzing the phosphate bond, the phosphate were transferred to some other molecule: alkaline phosphatase could act as a catalyst for such transfers.

It should, of course, be clear from what has been said above that we cannot at present do more than speculate about the function of alkaline phosphatase in the cell nuclei. There must also be considerable doubt as to whether it is at present profitable to speculate about this matter at all. At present we can determine the cytochemical localization of very few substances in the cell. In the nucleus we can determine pentose and deoxypentose nucleic acids and alkaline phosphatase with some degree of accuracy. But we can be reasonably confident that there are a vast number of other substances present in the nucleus. Until we know more about these other substances, only by the greatest of good fortune can any of our speculations concerning the functions of phosphatase and nucleic acid be correct.

PHOSPHATASE IN THE NUCLEI OF CILIATES

Dr. H. Mugard has studied a considerable variety of ciliates, using the alkaline phosphatase technique. The results may be exemplified by considering the two species, *Ophryoglena atra* and *Opalina ranarum* Stokes. With *Ophryoglena* no phosphatase is found in the starved animals. Immediately after the taking of food, phosphatase appears in the vicinity of the food vacuoles: this occurs within a few seconds of formation of the vacuoles. Very shortly afterwards phosphatase may also be observed in the macronucleus, micronucleus, and throughout the cytoplasm. Feeding is commonly followed by encystment. Following encystment the concentration of phosphatase falls in the cytoplasm, and the macronucleus becomes negative. The micronucleus continues strongly positive. But as divisions proceed within the cyst the amount of phosphatase in the micronucleus appears to diminish at every division.

With *Opalina* there is no phosphatase to be found in the cytoplasm unless division is occurring. The nuclei contain a considerable amount of phosphatase, particularly in the chromocentres, and the chromosomes found during mitosis are strongly positive.

Dr. Mugard inclines to the view expressed by Brachet, that alkaline phosphatase is related to the rate of deoxy nucleic acid turnover. It is, however, difficult to reconcile this view with the fact that alkaline phosphatase remains constant in amount in the sea-urchin egg until gastrulation occurs, whereas a considerable synthesis of deoxy nucleic acid occurs before gastrulation.

A more extended study of the relationships among nucleic acids, proteins, and alkaline phosphatases in Protozoa is required. The situation is becoming somewhat complicated by the fact that it appears unlikely that there is only one alkaline phosphatase. I have found that there is often a difference in properties between nuclear and cytoplasm phosphatase. Ross and Ely (1951) have recently made the very much more striking observation that there is a high tendency for substrate specificity with some nuclei. For example, with *Habrabracon* the nucleus contained no enzyme capable of reacting with glycerophosphate or with adenosine phosphate. On the other hand, adenosine diphosphate and triphosphate are both rapidly attacked by nuclear enzymes. They have also found that, in plant tissues where there is an apparent absence of glycerophosphatase (possibly due to hypersensitivity to fixatives), there is a vigorous reaction with certain nucleotides and not with others. So far as the evidence goes at the moment, we must contemplate the possibility that there may be many alkaline phosphates, which may be individually concerned with either nucleic acid or protein synthesis, or with both.

Alkaline Phosphatase, Protein Synthesis, and Differentiation

FORMATION OF FIBROUS PROTEINS

Fell and Danielli (1943) made a study of the action of some chemical warfare agents upon rat skin. In the course of this work, Miss Fell observed that at the site of a small healing skin lesion there was a very strong phosphatase reaction. A study was therefore made of the distribution of alkaline phosphatase in healing wounds. We observed that phosphatase occurred to a considerable concentration in proliferating cells, and that as new collagen was laid down a high concentration of phosphatase appeared apparently on the collagen fibres themselves. We also observed, as Bourne had done earlier, that phosphatase was present in the hair follicles and thus presumably was concerned in some way with the formation of fibrous keratin. On the other hand, we observed no indication that skin-keratin formation was associated with phosphatase activity. The association of formation of two fibrous proteins with alkaline phosphatase was suggestive, though it did not necessarily follow that there was any causal relationship between the two substances. To obtain further leads on this problem, we collaborated with Dr. Kodicek in a study of skin wounds in guinea pigs, both normal and vitamin-C-deficient animals being used. We found that there was a close parallelism between degree of vitamin C deficiency, the rate of formation of collagen, and the rate of appearance of alkaline phosphatase. We were surprised to find that the optimal rate of wound healing required a dosage of 10 milligrams of vitamin C per animal per day. Bourne (1943) had made some similar observations on the healing of cavities in bones. He observed that the first step was the formation of protein fibres in the cavity, and that these protein fibres were very rich in alkaline phosphatase.

We were unable to discover a causal connection between protein synthesis and alkaline phosphatase. It seemed, however, possible that one of the best methods of pursuing the matter would be to investigate the formation of other fibrous proteins such as silk. J. R. G. Bradfield has pursued this matter. Although he has not been able to establish the exact site of synthesis of silk proteins, he was able to show that the secreting cells of the glands which are actively engaged in secretion of silk protein have in one region of their cytoplasm, bordering on the lumen of the gland concerned, a high concentration of active phosphatase. On the other hand, Helen Brown, in a study of the formation of the protein which constitutes the byssus thread of *Mytilus,* has been unable to detect an association of the protein with alkaline phosphatase at any stage. This latter observation recalls the lack of association of skin keratin formation with alkaline phosphatase. On the other hand, in this connection it is notable that the horny teeth of *Myxine* and the horns of deer involved fibrous keratin formation associated with alkaline phosphatase.

THE MECHANISM OF BONE FORMATION

As was mentioned at the beginning of this chapter, Robison was able to establish that there was a close correlation between sites of bone formation and of the occurrence of alkaline phosphatase. Before bone could be formed, the mechanisms which had to be involved and which must operate simultaneously included the following:

(a) The formation of a matrix (cartilage in the case of cartilage bone).

(b) The formation of extracellular relatively indiffusible alkaline phosphatase.

(c) Development of a local concentration of phosphate esters.

(d) A process for reorganization of the initial amorphous precipitate of calcium phosphate which is produced under the action of factors a, b, and c, into compact bone.

One of the key points in this process must be production of phosphatase at the right point at the right time. It seemed impossible on theoretical grounds that intracellular phosphatase could be directly concerned in producing calcification.

The relationship between intracellular and extracellular phosphatase and calcification has been investigated by I. J. Lorch. The development of a number of membrane and cartilage bones was studied in trout larvae. With both types of bones, calcification is invariably produced by the formation of extracellular phosphatase. During the development of the larvae there are waves of occurrence of alkaline phosphatase in different regions. The phosphatase builds up to a considerable concentration and then over a few days falls to a much lower concentration. In the case of the formation of membrane or cartilage bone, there is a wave of development of intracellular phosphatase which is associated with the formation of the matrix. This intracellular phosphatase is not associated with bone formation and may largely disappear, to be succeeded by a second wave of formation of phosphatase, a great part of which is found outside the cells. This latter wave is followed by the deposition of extracellular calcium phosphate.

Studies were also made on the development of dogfish larvae. Factors a, b, and c were all found to be operative in the development of the larvae. In fact the phenomena were very similar to those observed in trout larvae at different stages of development:

waves of alkaline phosphatase occurred at different sites, including a wave of intracellular phosphatase during the formation of cartilage. But there was no calcification of the cartilage until extracellular phosphatase appeared in the cartilage.

In the calcification of fish scales and of teeth there is a similar development of phosphatase prior to calcification (Thorell and Wilton, 1945; Greep et al., 1948; Lorch, unpublished). It thus appears that the process of calcification, where the calcium is laid down as calcium phosphate, is invariably produced by the formation of extracellular phosphatase. The converse of this, however, is not necessarily true. There are probably many sites in which extracellular phosphatase is laid down in which no calcification occurs. These sites normally include healing wounds, though occasionally calcification will occur in a healing wound. It also appears that failure to form bone in the dogfish is not due to any deficiency in the calcification mechanism, but is due to a lack of the reorganization of amorphous calcium phosphatase into organized bone. This conclusion is, of course, readily compatible with the view that the cartilaginous skeleton of the dogfish is not primitive but has evolved by loss of one of the vital processes of bone formation. On the other hand, this state of affairs certainly does not prove that the cartilaginous fishes are not primitive, since the state of affairs found in their skeletons could represent either a loss of ability to reorganize calcium phosphate into bone, or a system in which this capacity has never been evolved.

It should perhaps be mentioned that it is not by any means clear by what mechanism a sufficient concentration of phosphate esters is produced in the calcifying regions to secure liberation of an adequate supply of phosphate by enzyme activity. It may be that a sufficient quantity of phosphate esters is normally present in the intercellular fluid. Some authorities have suggested that, since the cells in the calcifying regions are commonly rich in glycogen, what occurs is that sugar is stored in these cells and released as glucose phosphate or some other phosphate ester at the time of formation of calcium phosphate. This, however, cannot be the whole story, since, in order to form the phosphate ester, phosphate is also required. If, therefore, the function of glycogen found in calcifying regions is to provide a store of glucose for the formation of phosphate esters, it is also necessary that the cell should store phosphate, and that the phosphate ester should then be released in a wave over a brief period. It seems equally probable, so far as the evidence at present available is concerned, that the glycogen is not directly concerned in calcification. Indeed, it may even be that hydrolysis of phosphate esters (derived ultimately from the blood stream) in the cartilage raises the concentration of glycogen precursors to such an extent as to cause glycogen formation in cartilage cells as an indirect effect of calcification, i.e., that the phosphate moiety of the phosphate esters is being deposited as calcium phosphate in the cartilage while the other moiety of the molecule is being deposited as glycogen in the cartilage cells.

ALKALINE PHOSPHATASE AND DIFFERENTIATION

From the data which have been presented above there have been a number of hints that alkaline phosphatase may be concerned in certain steps at any rate in the process of differentiation. We know so little of the mechanism of differentiation that it is difficult to formulate a detailed suggestion as to how such an enzyme may be participating. The difficulty is enhanced by the fact that the same enzyme appears to operate both as a hydrolytic enzyme and as a phosphokinase. But, although it is not possible at the present time to produce a detailed physicochemical working hypothesis for the function of alkaline phosphatase in connection with differentiation, there is an impressive body of evidence that there is such a connection. Moog (1944) has shown that in the development of the chick there are waves of formation of alkaline phosphatase at different stages in the development of at least most tissues. Lorch (1949) has recorded a similar finding in the development of dogfish and trout. Yao (1950) has made a similar observation with Drosophila larvae. Runnström and his colleagues have also shown that there is a great increase in alkaline phosphatase concentration in echinoderm eggs immediately after gastrulation. This last observation is particularly striking in that it is not until after gastrulation occurs that a significant quantity of new antigens are formed in the development of the echinoderm larvae. It is at the same stage that nucleoli become prominent in the cells of the developing larvae: Caspersson and his colleagues have produced a good deal of evidence to show that prominence of nucleolar activity is associated with protein synthesis, and, as we have noted before, nucleoli are usually one of the most phosphatase-rich regions of a cell. On the other hand, it is not possible to maintain that there is a direct correlation between the cytochemically demonstrable alkaline phosphatase and protein synthesis in all cases. Thus, though some tumours are rich in alkaline phosphatase, other tumours which are growing equally rapidly, such as the Rous chicken carcinoma, contain relatively little phosphatase. We must also recall that the formation of skin keratin and of the byssus thread of *Mytilus* do not appear to be associated with alkaline phosphatase. It is, of course, possible that there are amounts of alkaline phosphatase in the cells carrying out syntheses of these last two proteins which are sufficient for the purposes of the cell but which are too small to be demonstrated cytochemically. Alternatively, it may be that with certain proteins the function performed by alkaline phosphatase is taken over by a more labile phosphatase. Whatever the explanation may be of the fact that presence of alkaline phosphatase cannot always be demonstrated in connection with protein synthesis, the fact remains that there is a very close correlation of occurrence of alkaline phosphatase with protein synthesis and with certain stages in differentiation. As Dale has said in connection with the correlation between liberation of acetylcholine at motor end plates and muscular contraction, it can hardly be that the correlation exists simply to mislead investigators! Further work, however, is essential in this field. As we shall see towards the end of this chapter, it is conceivable that the alkaline phosphatase is connected, not with *synthesis* of proteins, but with their *activities* immediately after synthesis. It may well be that studies on Protozoa along lines similar to those of Mugard will yield vital information.

Alkaline Phosphatase and Secretion

Verzar (1936) suggested that the process of secretion of substances across cell membranes might be connected with phosphorylation. Wilbrandt obtained some evidence for this by the use of enzyme poisons to inhibit secretion. His results have been confirmed by numerous other workers. It has also been shown that at many, if not all, sites of secretion of colloids, a high concentration of alkaline phosphatase is present. There were, however, many unsatisfactory features of this work. In the first place, the fact that enzyme poisons which interfere with phosphorylating processes also prevent secretion does not necessarily tell us very much about the actual process of secretion itself. The general metabolism of the cell is also based on phosphorylation, and consequently failure of secretory activity as a result of a poisoning of the phosphorylating mechanisms may simply indicate a general breakdown in cellular activities. Secondly, it was difficult to allot a function to alkaline phosphatase in connection with secretion, since it is fundamentally a dephosphorylating enzyme.

I pointed out in 1943 that, in any case, before a simple phosphorylating process can effect secretion it is necessary to have specific phosphorylating and dephosphorylating enzyme systems present in appropriate parts of cells. For example, for the secretion of glucose from the kidney the requirements are those indicated in Fig. 3. Consider the upper part of the figure, which illustrates the necessary siting of various enzyme systems. Since glucose phosphate permeates cells much more slowly than does glucose, it is necessary to have a dephosphorylating system on the external border of the tubule cells at A, so that any glucose phosphate in the tubule lumen is rapidly converted into glucose and phosphate ion. The same difference between the permeabilities of cells to glucose and glucose phosphate also determines the intracellular siting of enzymes if secretion is to occur. If glucose which has diffused into the tubule cells is converted immediately into glucose phosphate, the tendency to diffuse back into the tubule will be greatly reduced: consequently, a phosphorylating system is required in the cytoplasm adjacent to the lumen at B. The converse situation is required in the cytoplasm adjacent to the tissue spaces: i.e., to accelerate passage through the cell membrane glucose phosphate must be converted to glucose. Hence there must be a dephosphorylating system at C.

As a result of this distribution of enzyme systems, a pattern of concentrations of glucose and glucose phosphate will be built up as indicated in the lower part of Fig. 3. The net result of the action of the enzyme systems is that, inside the cell, there is a relatively high concentration of glucose against the membrane adjacent to the tissue spaces, and an equivalent concentration of glucose phosphate against the membrane adjacent to the lumen of the tubules. As glucose penetrates the cell wall much more rapidly than glucose phosphate, there will be a net transfer of glucose across the cell, and thus transfer of glucose from tubules

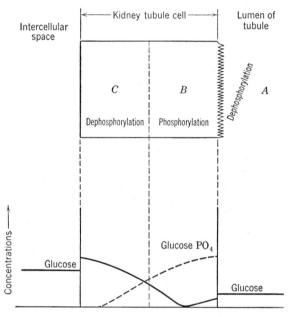

FIG. 3. The upper part of the figure shows the distribution of enzyme systems required to provide a secretory effect. The lower part of the figure shows the concentrations that will arise in the various parts of the system as a result of the enzyme actions.

to tissue spaces may be effected, even against a concentration gradient.

The mechanism detailed above considers only the secretion of glucose by kidney; in principle, of course, it can be extended to cover the secretion of almost any type of molecule.

The techniques for the study of alkaline phosphatase have made it possible to see to what extent this enzyme was present in the sites required by the working hypothesis indicated above. Gomori and Takamatsu showed that alkaline phosphatase occurs in the brush borders of the glucose-secreting kidney tubule cells in a variety of mammals. This has also been found to be the case with representative members of all the other vertebrate classes (see Moog, 1946, for a survey of the literature). The only case where there is alleged to be an absence of alkaline phosphatase is with the toad fish *Opsanus*, one specimen of which was studied by Wilmer. On the other hand, a number of species of aglomerular fishes were studied by Lorch and Danielli, who found that alkaline phosphatase was present in the border regions of the secreting cells in all cases. It seems possible that the observation upon *Opsanus* is in error; post-mortem changes occur very readily in the kidneys of fish. Whereas the detailed morphology of the excreting organs of invertebrates differs very markedly from that of the vertebrate kidney, the invertebrate excretory organs always contain regions which have either been proved to be, or are suspected to be, carrying out secretory processes closely analogous to those occurring in the vertebrate kidney. In all cases where these organs have been studied, these "secretory" regions are found to be rich in alkaline phosphatase at sites functionally analogous to the sites in mammalian kidney which are rich in alkaline phosphatase. This is the case for the nephridia of a terrestrial triclad (Pantin and Danielli, 1950), for the green gland of the crayfish *Camburus* (Kugler and Birkner, 1948), for the Malpighian tubules of the tick *Rhodnius*, and a number of insect larvae (Bradfield, 1950; Yao, 1950).

Apart from the excretory organs, numerous other sites of solute secretion contain alkaline phosphatase on the free border of the secretory cells which is exposed to the fluid from which the solute is to be removed. This is the case with the small intestine, the choroid plexus, the prostate gland, the placenta, etc. (for a review see Bradfield, 1950).

Thus there is an impressive body of evidence that alkaline phosphatase is associated with the selectively active borders of a wide variety of secretory cells. But it is still not clear whether the phosphatase is inside the plasma membrane or on the exterior of the cell. These two possibilities must be considered separately.

If the phosphatase is on the outside of the cells, it is in the position in which it can carry out the dephosphorylation A of the mechanism described on p. 69. But the situation is not particularly satisfactory, for there has so far been no indication of the existence of the other postulated enzyme systems at B and C.

On the other hand, it may be that the alkaline phosphatase is intracellular, and, in fact, acting as a phosphokinase in relation to secretion; if this is so, the enzyme found on the borders of cells must have the function of transferring phosphate molecules from a precursor such as adenosine triphosphate to substances such as glucose as soon as the latter penetrate into the cell, thus preventing back diffusion. Much more study is needed of the details of organization of this system before any further conclusions may be drawn.

SECRETION BY CONTRACTILE PROTEINS

In the meantime a quite different suggestion for a mechanism of secretion has been made by R. J. Goldacre. He has suggested that secretion is carried out by the folding and unfolding of protein molecules. His basic concept is that, when a protein molecule is extended or unfolded, groups are exposed which are able to adsorb specific molecules. Then, if later the protein molecule becomes folded, the adsorbing groups may saturate their affinities intramolecularly, so that the adsorbed molecules become desorbed. Impressive evidence that this may occur has been obtained by studying the adsorption of dyes on proteins. For example, globular serum albumin adsorbs comparatively small amounts of dyes, whereas when spread in a monolayer it adsorbs large amounts. Similar observations have been made on tobacco mosaic virus and other proteins. Consequently, we may consider it adequately demonstrated that the folding of proteins could be one of the basic processes in secretion. Is this process one which can be reconciled with experimental studies of secretion?

Now Osterhout has pointed out that a great deal of the data on the secretion of ions is not readily compatible with the idea that there is a rapid movement of ions through cell membranes by thermal diffusion. The evidence is more in favour of a one-way mechanism in which, for example, an ion such as potassium in the environment combines with a molecule of the cell membrane, following which the complex so formed diffuses across the membrane and discharges the ion into the interior of the cell. In some peculiar way no back diffusion occurs. With potassium, for example, as the external potassium concentration is raised the rate of transport of potassium decreases relative to the external concentration, indicating that there is a limited supply of the transporting molecules in the cell membrane.

If we consider Goldacre's proposal in the light of Osterhout's work and of the studies on phosphatase, it appears that we can meet the requirements of the situation by a model such as that in-

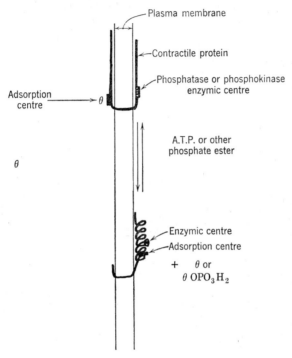

Plasma membrane

Contractile protein

Phosphatase or phosphokinase
enzymic centre

Adsorption
centre

θ

A.T.P. or other
phosphate ester

θ

Enzymic centre
Adsorption centre

$+ \quad \theta$ or
$\theta \, OPO_3H_2$

FIG. 4. Diagram to illustrate one of the possible mechanisms for transporting the substance θ across a membrane as the result of the action of a contractile enzyme.

dicated in Fig. 4. This model is based upon the view that the secretory activity is performed by the folding of a contractile protein, and that the contraction is brought about by reaction of the protein with a substance such as A.T.P. (adenosine triphosphate), as is the case with actomyosin. The phosphatase thus represents an enzymic centre through which the energy of A.T.P. is transferred to the contractile protein. In this model, as indicated on the upper part of the figure, the initial configuration of the protein has one part of an extended chain on the cytoplasmic side of the membrane, and the other part of the extended protein chain on the environmental side of the membrane. On the environmental side there is a specific adsorbing group which possesses a high affinity for the substance θ. If now A.T.P. comes into contact with the intracellular part of the protein, the protein contracts and folds, as indicated on the lower part of the figure. This contraction retracts the part of the protein chain containing the complex $R\theta$ from the external surface of the cell into the internal surface. On reaching the internal surface, the folding of the protein becomes such that the affinity of the adsorbing group can be satisfied by internal forces in the coiled protein molecule, so that the group θ is discharged into the interior of the cell.

There are a considerable number of possibilities for the details of such a mechanism. The contraction of a protein molecule under the action of A.T.P. is, of course, already well established in the case of the myosin-actin complex. One of the simplest working hypotheses would be that combination of the protein with A.T.P. results in coiling of the protein molecule so as to carry out the transference of θ. If, as is the case with myosin, the protein has phosphatase activity, the A.T.P. will eventually be split and extension of the protein will occur again so that the original configuration of the molecule is restored, and a fresh cycle of transfer of θ may occur. If the protein is acting as a simple phosphatase, inorganic phosphate will be split off. On the other hand, it may well be that the protein will act as a phosphokinase, in which case it may not be θ but the phosphate of θ (i.e., θOPO_3H_2) which is split off. It might well be that the process of splitting off a phosphorylated θ and the extension of the protein are simultaneous.

A mechanism such as that just suggested would provide a very adequate explanation of the close correlation of alkaline phosphatase and/or phosphokinase with sites of glucose transfer. That A.T.P. is involved would mean that the process is indirectly linked with respiration and/or glycolysis.

The mechanism which has been proposed above can be of very general application. The nature of the molecule which is transported would depend almost entirely on the affinity of the adsorbing group on the protein. Thus it should not be difficult for such a system, with appropriate variations in the adsorbing group, to transport such diverse molecules as sugar, potassium, amino acids, etc. It should also be quite possible for a modified form of this mechanism to secure removal of a substance from a cell, instead of secretion of a substance into a cell.

It is clear that investigation of the actual existence of the mechanism proposed above would be very much assisted if specific poisons were available for the alkaline phosphatases and phosphokinases, particularly those which may react with phosphorylating agents such as adenosine triphosphate.

Generalisation of the Contractile Protein Hypothesis

In this chapter alkaline phosphatase has been shown to be present in a variety of cellular sites, and to be fulfilling a variety of functions. It has been my endeavour to indicate that many alternative explanations must be considered in each case. But, to conclude this chapter, I wish to propose a unifying theory, i.e., a theory which would permit alkaline phosphatase to be concerned in a wide variety of activities, and yet to be acting in fundamentally the same way in all cases. *This theory is that the phosphatase usually represents the enzymic centre of a contractile protein.* The fundamental significance of the enzyme activity is the ability to make the chemical energy of a high-energy phosphate bond available for contraction of a protein.

In the preceding section of this book we have seen that this view, in conjunction with Goldacre's theory of the performance of osmotic work, affords a most interesting approach to the problems of secretion. We shall now consider the significance of phosphatase in relation to three other problems: (1) chromosomes, chromocentres and nucleoli; (2) collagen; (3) division spindles.

1. One of the most striking features of the behaviour of chromosomes is their contraction during mitosis and meiosis. The fact that chromosomes commonly have alkaline phosphatase, and that during mitosis they appear to be rich in phosphatase, appears to be compatible with the view that the contraction may be brought about by a process fundamentally similar to that responsible for the contraction of actomyosin. In the intermitotic

nucleus the richest sites of phosphatase are the chromocentres and particularly the nucleoli: in *Drosophila* salivary chromosomes the Feulgen-positive bands contain most of the nuclear phosphatase. It is probable that in the living cell all these regions are either in a steadily contracted state, or in a state of intermittent contraction. This latter suggestion has many points of interest. There is no reason to believe that intermitotic chromosomes are inert except so far as purely chemical processes are concerned. Contractility in active regions of chromosomes might well play a significant part in the shedding of gene products, or in effecting the folding of synthesized polypeptide chains into globular proteins.

2. The association of phosphatase with newly formed collagen, first discovered by H. B. Fell, has evoked many speculations as to its significance. To my view, none of these speculations have acted as a beacon by which a path for further advance could be plotted. But, if the significance of the association is that new collagen is a contractile protein, a new way does become clear. One of the most dramatic phenomena in the healing of a wound is the contraction which occurs as new collagen is laid down. This contraction occurs at the time at which the collagen is rich in phosphatase. In vitamin C deficiency, although much fibrous protein is formed in a healing wound, no phosphatase is found, and no contraction occurs. If newly formed connective-tissue protein is normally contractile, we may indeed expect the contractility to be of marked physiological importance. For example, in organizing the structure of bone, collagen contractility may be involved.

3. Although alkaline phosphatase has been observed to be associated with the centrosome and spindles, it has not yet been demonstrated by critical studies that this represents intrinsic phosphatase. But if there is in fact phosphatase in these positions in the living cell, we should again be provided with a new route of inquiry into the nature of spindle action.

Thus it may be seen that, although the cytochemical study of enzymes is at present conducted on a relatively crude basis, it bears many signs of being a skeleton key which will open many of Nature's locks. With increasingly critical usage, we are likely to find in such studies a far more delicate weapon than are the common methods of biochemistry.

REFERENCES

AXELROD. 1948. *J. Biol. Chem.*, *172*, 1.
BRADFIELD. 1950. *Biol. Revs.*, *25*, 113.
BOURNE. 1943. *Quart. J. Exp. Physiol.*, *32*, 1.
BROWN, H. Personal Communication.
CASPERSSON. 1950. *Cell Growth and Cell Function* (Norton, New York).
DANIELLI. 1943. In *The Permeability of Natural Membranes*, by Davson and Danielli (University Press, Cambridge).
DANIELLI. 1946. *J. Exp. Biol.*, *22*, 110.
    1950*a*. *Cold Spring Harbor Symposia*, *14*, 32.
    1950*b*. *XIII⁰ Congrès international de zoologie*, 205 (Protar, Paris).
    1951. *Nature* (in press).
DANIELLI and CATCHESIDE. 1945. *Nature*, *156*, 294.
FELL AND DANIELLI. 1943. *Brit. J. Exp. Path.*, *24*, 196.
GOLDACRE AND LORCH. 1950. *Nature*, *166*, 497.
GOMORI. 1939. *Proc. Soc. Exp. Biol.*, *New York*, *42*, 23.
GREEP et al. 1948. *J. Am. Dental Assoc.*, *36*, 467.
KODICEK, FELL, AND DANIELLI. 1945. *Brit. J. Exp. Path.*, *26*, 367.
KRUGELIS. 1942. *J. Cell. Comp. Physiol.*, *20*, 374.
    1945. *Genetics*, *30*, 12.
KUGLER AND BIRKNER. 1948. *Physiol. Zool.*, *21*, 105.
LORCH. 1949. *Quart. J. Micro. Sci.*, *90*, 183, 381.
LOVELESS AND DANIELLI. 1949. *Quart. J. Micro. Sci.*, *90*, 57.
MARTIN AND JACOBY. 1949. *Nature*, *163*, 875.
MENTEN, JUNGE, AND GREEN. 1944. *J. Biol. Chem.*, *153*, 471.
MEYERHOFF AND GREEN. 1950. *J. Biol. Chem.*, *183*, 377.
MOOG. 1944. *Biol. Bull.*, *86*, 51.
    1946. *Biol. Rev.*, *21*, 41.
MUGARD. 1953. *Quart. J. Micros. Sci.* (in press).
DE NICOLA. 1949. *Quart. J. Micro. Sci.*, *90*, 391.
OSTERHOUT. 1951. *Biol. Bull.* (in press).
PANTIN AND DANIELLI. 1950. *Quart. J. Micro. Sci.*, *41*, 209.
ROBISON. 1923. *Biochem. J.*, *17*, 286.
ROSS AND ELY. 1951. *Exp. Cell Research*, *2*, 339.
RUNNSTRÖM. Personal Communication.
SAUNDERS. 1936. *The Aromatic Diazo Compounds* (Arnold, London).
TAKAMATSU. 1939. *Trans. Path. Soc. Japan*, *29*, 492.
THORELL AND WILTON. 1945. *Acta Path. Microbiol. Scand.*, *22*, 5.
VERZAR AND MACDOUGAL. 1936. *Absorption from the Intestine* (Longmans, Green, London).
WILLMER. 1942. *J. Exp. Biol.*, *19*, 11.
WILMER. 1944. *Arch. Path.*, *37*, 227.
YAO. 1950. *Quart. J. Micro. Sci.*, *91*, 79, 89.

CHAPTER 4

THE CRITICAL STUDY OF
THE CYTOCHEMISTRY OF ALDEHYDES

Introduction

Techniques will be considered which permit the study of the following types of aldehydes and derivatives of aldehydes:

1. Free aldehydes. Many tissues contain substances which have a very reactive aldehyde group. This generally forms part of a fatty molecule.

2. Another common component of tissues is aldehyde existing in the form of acetal.

3. Most sugars contain potential aldehyde groups of sugars which, however, are masked by ring formation. If at any time the ring opens, the aldehyde group becomes reactive.

4. In addition to the aldehyde groups just mentioned, which exist intrinsically in tissues, many recently developed cytochemical techniques involve formation of aldehyde groups developed as a result of oxidation procedures.

The most successful reagent for studying these compounds is reduced fuchsin, which was introduced by Feulgen, first for the study of nucleic acid and later for the study of free fatty aldehydes. The chemical properties of the different groups of aldehydes mentioned above permit distinctions to be made between them. Thus the reaction between reduced and free aldehydes is rapid and may be complete in 15 minutes or less. The acetal aldehydes can be split so as to release free aldehydes by a brief treatment with 0.1 N hydrochloric acid. There is a great deal of evidence that some of the tissue acetals can be split by the action of mercury salts. But, as mercury may have other actions besides that of splitting acetals, it is better to avoid mercury, and to use hydrolysis with dilute hydrochloric acid as the diagnostic procedure for acetals. Some glycosides may also be split by an appropriate hydrolysis. In the case of the deoxy sugars the aldehyde group of a sugar liberated from the glycoside will react in the cold with reduced fuchsin: This latter reaction is, of course, the basis for the Feulgen reaction for thymonucleic acid. Other sugars will react with reduced fuchsin at higher temperatures, but this procedure has not yet been studied in connection with cytochemistry. There is a sharp distinction between the hydrolysis conditions which will liberate free aldehydes from acetal and that required for splitting most glycosides—the acetals are liberated by a brief hydrolysis with 0.1 N acid in the cold, whereas most glycosides need much more vigorous treatment. The action of 0.1 N hydrochloric acid which is sufficient to complete the liberation of aldehyde from acetal has no significant effect in liberating purine from thymonucleic acid. Consequently, the two steps in hydrolysis give a clear-cut separation of these two types of aldehyde.

It is very important with all these techniques to avoid conditions under which oxidation of a tissue component may occur, for then adventitious aldehyde groups may appear in the tissue. Protection against this may to a large degree be secured by using a reducing substance such as formaldehyde as a component of the fixative, by carrying out the steps prior to exposure to reduced fuchsin under anaerobic conditions as far as possible, and by avoiding the presence of oxidising substances such as mercury and dichromate in the fixative. There seems to be no advantage gained by using oxidising agents other than periodate when it is wished to oxidise groups in tissue. Periodate is a fairly specific oxidising agent for glycols and β-hydroxyamines. Other oxidising agents which have been used, such as mercury and permanganate, are not sufficiently specific in their action to be very valuable in cytochemistry.

In the examination of tissue sections for aldehydes we must, of course, conform with the usual requirements of cytochemistry. Thus it is necessary to demonstrate:

1. That the aldehyde is present in fixed tissue in its physiologically normal position.
2. That the colour in the cytochemical reaction produced is indeed specific for aldehydes.
3. That no significant degree of destruction of aldehyde occurs during the procedure.
4. That the colour developed in the cytochemical reaction remains in the physiologically normal site of the aldehyde, and has not diffused to some other part of the tissue.

STANDARD TECHNIQUE

In any detailed investigation it is, of course, necessary to employ a considerable number of variations in technique. But it is convenient in making preliminary investigations to have a standard technique. The technique which will be given demonstrates the sum of free aldehyde and acetal aldehyde. Frozen sections must be used. The normal procedure of infiltration with wax will remove practically all the free fatty aldehyde and fatty acetal aldehyde. It is this which enables the Feulgen technique for thymonucleic acid to be carried out without masking by other aldehydes. The steps for demonstration of the sum of acetal and free aldehyde are as follows:

1. Sections of tissue not more than 2 millimeters in thickness are fixed in a solution containing 8 percent formaldehyde and 5 percent acetic acid.

2. After a minimum of 2 hours' fixation, frozen sections are cut.

3. The sections are washed with distilled water and then placed in cold 0.1 N hydrochloric acid for not more than 15 minutes. This liberates aldehyde from any acetal aldehyde present.

4. The sections are washed in distilled water to remove hydrochloric acid.

5. Sections are transferred to reduced fuchsin for 15 minutes.

6. The sections are given three washings, each of 5 minutes, in a solution containing sulfur dioxide. The sulfur dioxide solution can be prepared conveniently by mixing 10 milliliters of 10 percent sodium bisulfite solution with 10 milliliters of N hydrochloric acid, and adding distilled water to 200 milliliters.

7. The sections are washed in distilled water and mounted in glycerol or Canada balsam.

The fixative has been chosen because it gives a reasonable compromise between good fixation of cytoplasm and good fixation of the nucleus in many tissues. Other tissues may need a modified form of this fixative: for example, it may perhaps be necessary to make the fixative up in sea water for the tissues of marine animals. The high formaldehyde content is valuable in protecting free aldehyde against oxidation. The whole procedure up to step 5 can also be carried out when necessary under anaerobic conditions. This is most conveniently done by carrying out the treatment with fixative, etc., with the material in a Thunberg tube. The frozen sections can, if necessary, be cut in a closed box in an atmosphere of nitrogen. It is best to cut sections as soon as possible after fixation is complete. With some material, such as rat liver, a prolonged period of fixation does not seem to result in the production of artefacts. But as Cain and others have emphasized, artefacts probably due to oxidation arise rather readily in some tissues; I have found this to be the case with a number of tumor tissues.

Cain has suggested that a better technique is to use very small pieces of tissue which are placed, without previous fixation, in a mixture containing mercury and reduced fuchsin. With the tissues which I have studied, fixation under these circumstances tends to be very poor. But in any case there is always, with techniques of this type in which the colour due to a cytochemical reaction is produced in a block of tissue, the fundamental objection that it is impossible to study the extent to which the results are invalidated by diffusion phenomena. It is my view that a cytochemical technique which does not permit the evaluation of diffusion artefacts is useless.

After a preliminary survey of a tissue made by the procedure given above, the other points mentioned in the introduction to this chapter may then be studied as seems appropriate.

STUDY OF THE ACTION OF FIXATIVES

Where the substance which is being studied can safely be passed through an infiltration with wax, freeze-drying is the best method of fixation. But, for many tissue aldehydes, organic solvents must be avoided since they dissolve fatty aldehyde material from the tissue.

When freeze-drying cannot be employed it is necessary to use a variety of fixatives to investigate the degree to which the distribution of aldehyde is produced as a fixation artefact, as discussed in Chapter 2. It is possible to use acid, neutral, and alkaline fixatives, reducing fixatives, and preprecipitation with strong salt solutions in the study of fixation artefacts. There are, of course, limitations encountered in the use of this variety of fixatives with particular types of aldehyde. Thus an acid fixative is likely to liberate aldehyde from acetals, after which acetal adehyde and free aldehyde are, of course, indistinguishable.

As an example of the use of this method, we may consider studies which have been made of the fatty aldehydes of liver. When this material is placed in fixatives containing mixtures of formaldehyde, acetic acid, mercuric chloride, pyridine, and trichloracetic acid, either before or after preprecipitation of the tissue with saturated calcium chloride, magnesium sulfate, or ammonium sulfate, no variation in the distribution of aldehyde was found except with those fixatives containing trichloracetic acid. With the trichloracetic fixatives, after treatment with reduced fuchsin, some degree of nuclear staining was found which was not encountered with the other fixatives. It seems likely that this staining is caused by hydrolysis of the nuclear thymonucleic acid, since trichloracetic acid is a fairly strong acid. Apart from the nuclear staining, the aldehyde contained in the liver after treatment with these different fixatives is always in the same position, and it can always be removed by extraction with acetone. It therefore seems justifiable to conclude that this aldehyde is not shifted from its physiological position by the action of the fixative, with the reservation that strongly acid fixatives, such as those containing trichloracetic acid, must be avoided.

SPECIFICITY OF THE DETECTION OF ALDEHYDES

Of the naturally occurring compounds, there is no evidence that any other than aldehydes will react with reduced fuchsin to give a purple colour. Some unsaturated substances have been alleged to react, but the reaction appears to be due to the presence of aldehydes or other products of oxidation, and not to the original substance. This is the case with oleic acid. A few substances, such as those formed by atmospheric oxidation of substances containing double bonds, may perhaps be capable of reacting with reduced fuchsin to give colours similar to those given by aldehydes. But there is no evidence that such substances normally occur in tissues in an amount which would be detected in a cytochemical study. However, there always exists the possibility that some unusual substance may be encountered or that a reaction with reduced fuchsin may occur as a result of the presence of enzyme systems. Consequently, a number of supplementary tests which can be used to check the nature of the reacting substance are desirable. A number of reactions have been tried for this purpose. They include the following procedures.

1. A useful distinction can be made between substances which are soluble in fat solvents and those which are not. For example, it is important in the study of fat metabolism to be able to distinguish between the long-

chain fatty aldehydes and aldehydes which may be present in sugars, etc. Extraction with acetone is a convenient way of distinguishing between these two classes of substances. It is necessary, however, to carry out the extractions on tissue sections, for with thicker pieces of tissue very prolonged treatment is necessary to secure complete removal of lipoidal aldehyde.

2. Another substance which reacts with aldehydes in a fairly specific manner is azobenzene phenylhydrazine sulfonic acid. This substance reacts with aldehydes to give a purple colour. The purple colour is fully developed only in rather strong acid; consequently permanent mounts cannot be made. But the colour reaction is very useful for checking results obtained by the reduced-fuchsin method. This reagent also reacts with ketones, but not to give a purple colour.

3. Aldehydes readily reduce alkaline silver solutions to give a black precipitate of metallic silver. This reaction, however, is not very sensitive and can only be expected to be found at sites containing a high concentration of aldehyde. Ability to reduce alkaline silver solutions is not, of course, restricted to aldehydes: many substances will carry out this reduction. On the other hand, any substance which is an aldehyde *must* reduce alkaline silver.

4. A very useful group of reagents introduced by Bennett (1940) are the hydrazines. Phenylhydrazine itself does not give a deeply coloured compound with aldehyde groups, and indeed it is possible that it may be a useful compound for blocking free aldehyde groups. But 2:4 dinitro phenylhydrazine gives a fairly deep yellow colour with aldehydes. This reagent will also react with keto groups and is, therefore, not to be regarded as specific for aldehydes. Camber (1949) has introduced another hydrazine which can be used for obtaining more intense colouration, using techniques similar to those described in Chapter 5.

5. A very useful procedure is to block the aldehyde group by prior treatment with hydroxylamine or dimedone. When treated with one of these reagents before treatment with the reduced fuchsin, the aldehyde group is blocked up and no purple colour develops in the reduced fuchsin. It is probable that for many purposes dimedone is the better substance to use as a blocking agent, for L. G. Bell has shown that during the reaction with hydroxylamine the reagent solution may remove considerable amounts of the protein from the tissue section. Dimedone can be used in alcoholic solution, in which proteins do not dissolve readily.

Details of the reactions given above are provided elsewhere (Danielli, 1949a).

DESTRUCTION OF ALDEHYDE

It is always desirable to be sure that the aldehyde which is being studied in an experiment is not being destroyed by a particular step in the experimental procedure. This can be done simply by increasing the duration of each step in the procedure by a factor of, say, fourfold. If there is no significant difference in the intensity of the reaction which is found, there cannot be a significant loss of activity in any of the steps. Thus with liver tissue it has been found that the procedure given on page 80 does not cause any destruction of liver aldehyde.

THE DETECTION OF DIFFUSION ARTEFACTS

The amount of attention which has been paid to the elimination of diffusion artefacts in the cytochemistry of aldehydes is very small. Indeed, it may be said that most investigators have displayed a remarkable resistance even to considering the possibility that their results may be complicated by diffusion artefacts. Stedman and Stedman (1943) performed a very valuable service when they drew attention to the fact that the procedure of hydrolysis in N hydrochloric acid depolymerizes thymonucleic acid and suggested that this depolymerization may perhaps in some cases be sufficiently serious to make the nucleic acid diffusible. Following the observations of the Stedmans, I was able to show that, when purified thymonucleic acid is treated by the Feulgen method, a readily soluble fraction is formed. The procedure was simply to suspend thymonucleic acid in N hydrochloric acid at 60° C. After hydrolysis for 10 minutes the suspension was filtered, the filtrate neutralized, and reduced fuchsin solution added. A deep purple colour immediately developed. This coloured solution readily stains tissue sections and such preparations as squashes of *Drosophila* salivary glands. The distribution of stain in these specimens is very similar to that found in the Feulgen reaction, except that the nucleolus is more deeply stained than is normally found, and there also may be some staining of the cytoplasm. It is, therefore, difficult to be certain, without the use of diffusion studies, whether the results obtained by the fuchsin technique for thymonucleic acid are complicated by diffusion artefacts. This is particularly true so far as the fine detail of distribution of thymonucleic acid is concerned. It would not be difficult in any given instance to discover whether a significant amount of diffusion does in fact occur, if the superimposed section technique, referred to in earlier chapters of this book, were used. But I am not aware of any instance in which this procedure has in fact been used. It is likely that any diffusion artefact which does occur would be eliminated, or at least greatly reduced in magnitude, if the various steps in the procedure of Feulgen are, as far as possible, carried out in the presence of a heavy metal such as mercury. The heavy metal salts of the nucleic acids are very much less soluble than the free acids themselves.

A somewhat similar situation has been found with the long-chain fatty aldehydes. If a piece of liver tissue is ground with fat solvents, such as acetone, aldehyde present in the liver goes into solution in the acetone. If this acetone is now quickly shaken with a large volume of water, a colloidal solution of the aldehyde is obtained. On addition of reduced fuchsin to this solution, a deep purple colour develops. When tissues containing no aldehyde are exposed to this solution, the purple colour is taken up vigorously by the tissues. The distribution of colour so found, however, differs remarkably from that found for aldehyde in most tissues, in that the nuclei tend to be deeply stained whereas the cytoplasm is usually not very well stained. Thus, if liver tissue is stained for the aldehyde intrinsically present, practically all the aldehyde is found in the cytoplasm. If, however, all intrinsic aldehyde is removed from a liver section by treatment with acetone, and this section is then stained by the dye solution mentioned above, the staining of the section is largely retricted to the nucleus. Thus with the fatty aldehydes it is usually not difficult to demonstrate that the results are not complicated by diffusion artefacts, since the sites having a high affinity for the cytochemical reaction products differ significantly from the sites in which the reaction products are in fact found.

The use of superimposed sections provides a further very adequate check on the diffusibility of the aldehydes and their cytochemical reaction products.

PROCEDURES FOR DISTINGUISHING BETWEEN FREE ALDEHYDE, ACETAL ALDEHYDE, AND ALDEHYDE FORMED BY OXIDATION

When it is desired to distinguish between free aldehyde and acetal aldehyde, it is necessary to fix with a neutral fixative such as neutral formaldehyde solution. Table VI shows the general plan of procedures, using material which has been fixed in a neutral fixative.

TABLE VI

Distinction between free aldehyde, acetal aldehyde, and aldehyde liberated by oxidation. The numbers indicate the order in which the steps should be carried out to obtain a reaction for one only of the three types of aldehyde.

	Free Aldehyde	Acetal Aldehyde	Oxidation Aldehyde
Cold 0.1 N HCl	..	2	1
Oximation	..	1	2
Oxidation	..	..	3
Reduced fuchsin	1	3	4

To demonstrate free aldehyde only, the only procedure which is necessary after cutting frozen sections is to expose the sections to reduced fuchsin. This exposure should be of as short a duration as possible, and care must be taken that the fuchsin solution is not too acid in reaction. It frequently happens that part of the sulfur dioxide present in reduced fuchsin solution becomes oxidised to sulfuric acid, thus making the solution much more acid than it should be. It may be that, when free aldehyde alone is to be demonstrated, it is best to use a buffered solution of reduced fuchsin. However, I have not investigated this point.

To demonstrate acetal aldehyde only, the first step is to block up the free aldehyde with either hydroxylamine or dimedone. When this has been done, aldehyde is liberated from acetal by treatment with cold 0.1 N hydrochloric acid, and the aldehyde so liberated is coloured by treatment with reduced fuchsin.

To demonstrate aldehyde formed by oxidation procedures, it is first desirable to eliminate both free aldehyde and acetal aldehyde. The procedure in such a case is first to expose to cold 0.1 N hydrochloric acid, to liberate aldehyde from acetal. Then all the liberated and free aldehyde is blocked by treatment with hydroxylamine or dimedone. After this, the oxidation procedure may be carried through and then the aldehyde formed by oxidation may be demonstrated by treatment with reduced fuchsin.

Many of the papers on the cytochemical demonstration of aldehydes are extremely difficult to interpret, owing to the failure of the authors to distinguish clearly between free aldehyde, acetal aldehyde, and aldehyde formed by oxidation, both adventitious and intentional. Part of the difficulty has been, as Feulgen and

Voigt found, that acetal aldehyde in tissues is rather readily broken down to free aldehyde by mercury solutions. It is probable that mercury and other heavy metals can sometimes accelerate oxidation processes, so that when mercury is used an artefact is introduced, owing to oxidation of substances in tissues which would not otherwise give an aldehyde reaction. This difficulty is not encountered if fixatives and reagents devoid of mercury are used, as in the procedure described above.

The situation has also been somewhat complicated by the claim of Dempsey, Bunting, and Wislocki that α-hydroxy-β-keto-steroids may also be oxidised by cold aqueous mercuric solution with the formation of aldehydes. This is very unlikely to occur. Boscott, Mandl, Danielli, and Shoppee showed that when pure deoxycorticosterone is treated with aqueous mercuric chloride there is no indication of oxidation of the steroid. Deoxycorticosterone is a typical α,β-hydroxyketone. We may, therefore, say with confidence that typical α,β-hydroxy steroids will not be oxidized in the manner postulated by Dempsey et al. There remains, of course, the possibility that there may be some very atypical hydroxyketones which would react with cold aqueous mercuric chloride. However, if the procedure given above (pp. 85 and 86) is carried through there is no danger of complication from such atypical compounds. It must, however, be emphasized that the claim that hydroxyketosteroids have been demonstrated in tissues such as the adrenal gland, by the use of mercury solutions as an oxidising agent, must be discounted until the presence of atypical substances is in fact demonstrated by orthodox chemical means.

It should perhaps again be emphasized that one of the most important control experiments in the study of aldehydes is to carry a sample of tissue through the various steps of fixation etc., under anaerobic conditions, to eliminate the formation of aldehydes, or substances which may react like aldehydes, by atmospheric oxidation of tissue components. Cain, following the observations of Gomori and other workers, has quite correctly drawn attention to the danger of encountering artefacts due to atmospheric oxidation. But the procedures suggested by Cain do not offer any satisfactory means of eliminating both this and other artefacts. The procedure recommended above on the other hand should enable all the various artefacts to be distinguished clearly.

Aldehydes in Fat Transport and Metabolism

INTRODUCTON

Feulgen and Voigt (1924) showed that aldehydes of fatty type were to be found in many biological materials. My interest in these substances was aroused by the fact that the Rous chicken sarcoma virus is said to contain a considerable quantity of acetal aldehyde. Thus there appears to be a possibility that Rous virus could be localized in cells by analysis of the distribution of aldehyde. A preliminary examination of this possibility was made together with Dr. L. M. J. Rinaldini. We found that the situation was complicated by the fact that the Rous tumour is characteristically heavily infiltrated with fat, and that there appeared to be an association between fat droplets and sites of high aldehyde activity, particularly in the necrotic areas. As will be seen later, there can be no doubt that aldehydes are intimately concerned with fat metabolism, so that the occurrence of long-chain aldehydes in the Rous tumour can hardly be taken as diagnostic for the localization of virus. It may be, of course, that sites containing the aldehyde are also rich in virus, and that one of the major consequences of infection of cells with the Rous virus is a disturbance of fat metabolism.

Comparatively little is known of the steps involved in the synthesis and degradation of the higher fatty acids, such as palmitic or stearic acid. It is known that the naturally occurring fatty acids almost invariably contain an even number of carbon atoms and that, when the fatty acids are degraded, they usually lose carbon two atoms at a time. A suggestion which has, therefore, been considered in connection with fat synthesis is that it proceeds by the condensation of aldehydes, with acetaldehyde as the main condensing agent, in an aldol reaction:

$$R \cdot CH_2 \cdot CHO + CH_3 \cdot CHO \rightarrow R \cdot CH_2 \cdot CHOH \cdot CH_2 \cdot CHO$$

The biochemists have not found it possible to find acetaldehyde performing this function in tissues. However, it is quite certain that some 2-carbon compound, perhaps acetyl phosphate, or a free radical related to acetyl phosphate, is a main intermediate in the synthesis and degradation of fats. It is, therefore, of considerable interest in connection with fat metabolism as a whole to consider the function which may be performed by long-chain aldehydes. These substances have been unduly neglected by the biochemists, possibly because they so readily undergo polymerization and oxidation when treated by the common methods for examination of fats.

It was decided to study this problem in the liver of rats and mice. A concurrent study was also made of aldehyde in relation to absorption of fat from the digestive tract.

The material used in these experiments was fixed either in neutral formaldehyde or in 8 percent formaldehyde + 5 percent acetic acid.

ABSORPTION OF FAT FROM THE DIGESTIVE TRACT

Mice were fed with either emulsified olive oil or emulsified oleic acid; they were killed at intervals up to 7 hours after feeding; and various sections of the small intestine were examined. The fat droplets found in the intestinal epithelial cells were usually completely lacking in aldehyde, especially when a considerable amount of fat had been fed to the animals. When mice were fed on a diet containing a significant but small amount of fat, the occasional droplets of fat which are found in the cells often contain a considerable amount of aldehyde, and there may be a considerable amount of aldehyde distributed diffusely in the cytoplasm of the epithelial cells. But, when there is a considerable flow of fat droplets through the cells, no aldehyde can be observed. It thus seems clear that long-chain aldehydes are not concerned with either the absorption of fat or fatty acid into the cells, or with the transport of fat or fatty acids through these cells.

FAT METABOLISM IN THE LIVER

The results obtained depended somewhat on the diet. When the diet contained fat, protein, and carbohydrates, considerable areas of the liver, as seen in tissue sections, contained a diffuse distribution of aldehyde in the cytoplasm. There appeared to be no free aldehyde in the nucleus. When the cells contained fat droplets, each droplet appeared to be surrounded by a spherical shell containing a high concentration of aldehyde. There were also large areas of the liver sections which appeared to be free from aldehyde. These areas were also lacking in fat droplets.

When the animals were placed on a diet rich in fat, there was an increase in the number of fat droplets to be seen in the hepatic cells, and a concomitant increase in the amount of aldehyde found in the liver. All the droplets were surrounded by a spherical shell of aldehyde (e.g., Plate XII, Fig. A).

Some animals were also starved up to 6 days, although allowed free access to water. It is known that under such conditions fat passes from the fat depots of the body to the liver, where it is broken down into carbohydrates. It was found that under these circumstances the liver becomes heavily infiltrated with fat, and gives an intense aldehyde reaction, with a high concentration of aldehyde as a spherical shell surrounding the fat droplets. This result and the result recorded in the preceding paragraph make it clear that long-chain aldehyde is closely connected with the conversion of fat to carbohydrate.

Another group of animals was fed on a diet containing protein and a high concentration of carbohydrate, but no fat. It is known from isotope experiments that under these conditions no fat is lost from the fat depots, and that fat is synthesized in the liver from carbohydrate. When animals were killed at various times after being placed on this carbohydrate-rich diet, it was found that the initial response was a sharp decline in the amount of aldehyde in the liver, together with the loss of fat drops from the liver. After 2 or 3 days on this diet, a considerable amount of aldehyde appeared diffusely distributed in the cytoplasm. Fat droplets reappeared and were closely associated as a general rule with a spherical shell of aldehyde. Some fat droplets, however, did not contain aldehyde. On this diet aldehyde was also frequently found in the bile canaliculi. It was concluded that it was probable that there is also a close connection between long-chain aldehydes and fat synthesis, although the evidence for this is not quite so strong as is the case for the relationship between fat degradation and long-chain aldehydes.

All the experiments reported above, both those on the liver and those on the intestine, were performed on material which had been fixed for little more than 2 hours. The intensity of the aldehyde reaction was not influenced by conducting fixation, etc., under anaerobic conditions.

THE NATURE OF FAT SYNTHESIS AND DEGRADATION

The following group of facts needs to be considered in relation to fat synthesis and degradation:

1. Long-chain aldehydes are intimately connected with fat metabolism in the liver.
2. The fat droplets found in tumours are also commonly associated with long-chain aldehyde.
3. When fat appears in tissue cultures the droplets are commonly surrounded by a shell of aldehyde.
4. Biochemical evidence shows that changes in fat are mainly mediated by loss or addition, not of CO_2, but of 2-carbon fragments.
5. Whereas free fatty acid is not attacked by liver extracts, the acyl phosphates are readily attacked by such extracts (Lehninger, 1945).

There are a number of questions the answers to which are far from clear at the present time in connection with the function of the aldehyde. Thus we do not know whether the aldehyde involved occurs as a true intermediate, as an end-product or as a by-product of processes occurring in the liver. If it is a true intermediate, we must envisage a series of reactions in which aldehydes, or compounds such as acetals which readily give rise to aldehydes, are involved in synthesis and degradation of at least the higher fatty acids (Danielli, 1950b), and occur as part of the process of β-oxidation.

It must, of course, be pointed out that we do not know whether the aldehyde which is involved in fat metabolism occurs as free aldehyde, as aldehyde acetal, or as some other compound of aldehydes. One possibility is that the true intermediate is aldehyde phosphate such as $R \cdot CHOH \cdot OPO_3H_2$. This last compound would be highly reactive and unstable in the presence of water, and so it would be difficult to discover in tissues. If it occurred as a true intermediate, one would probably find by cytochemical processes either free aldehyde derived from its decomposition, or, as we shall see later, an acetal. It is clear that there is room for a considerable amount of work, particularly on the enzymes which might be associated with reactions involving aldehydes. At the present no methods have been worked out for the cytochemical localization of such enzymes. But it is interesting to note that Worden (1943) has found that there is a very high concentration of aldehyde oxidase present in adsorbed form on the surface of the fat droplets of milk.

THE SIGNIFICANCE OF ALDEHYDE ACETAL

Feulgen and his colleagues showed that, whereas some free aldehyde (which they originally called plasmal) exists in tissues, a large part of the naturally occurring aldehyde occurs as the acetal phosphate of glycerol (which they called plasmalogen), as shown in Formula III. The acetal phosphate III has been shown to be a common constituent of tissues. Its mode of formation is not at present clear. If an aldehyde phosphate occurs in tissues, it might well combine spontaneously with glycerol as indicated in I, to give the compound II. This latter compound would probably pass spontaneously into III by wandering of the phosphate radical, as occurs in the equilibrium between α- and β-glycerophosphates. Alternatively, it may be that the compound III is derived by condensation of free aldehyde and glycerophosphate to give the acetal phosphate. Various hypotheses could be put forward for the function of the acetal compound III. It might be concerned in fatty-acid metabolism, in the formation of triglycerides or in the formation of phospholipins. But there is little evidence available on these points as yet.

$$
\begin{array}{ccc}
\begin{array}{c}
R \\
| \\
CH \\
\diagup \quad \diagdown \\
OH \qquad OPO_3H_2 \\
+ \\
HO \qquad OH \\
| \qquad | \\
CH_2\!-\!CH\!-\!CH_2OH \\
\text{I}
\end{array}
&
\rightarrow
\begin{array}{c}
R \\
| \\
CH \\
\diagup \quad \diagdown \\
O \qquad OPO_3H_2 \\
| \\
\quad OH \\
\quad | \\
CH_2\!-\!CH\!-\!CH_2OH_2 \\
\text{II}
\end{array}
& \rightarrow
\end{array}
$$

$$
\begin{array}{c}
R \\
| \\
CH \\
\diagup \quad \diagdown \\
O \qquad O \\
| \qquad | \\
CH_2\!-\!-\!CH\!-\!CH_2OPO_3H_2 \\
\text{III}
\end{array}
$$

THE STUDY OF GLYCOLS IN TISSUES

Groups such as $-CHOH-CHOH-$ do not react directly with any of the reagents for aldehydes. Recently, however, it has been shown that periodate reacts in a fairly specific manner with these groups, to form aldehyde groups which may then be detected with the aldehyde reagents. Hotchkiss has shown that treatment with periodate may be a very valuable procedure in the study of carbohydrates in tissues, provided that the carbohydrates are insoluble in water (see, for example, Plate XII, Fig. B). This technique has at present been far less extensively exploited than is desirable. There is a possibility that it could be used to demonstrate the presence of pentose nucleic acid. Normally a nucleic acid does not contain an α,β-glycol grouping. After hydrolysis of pentose nucleic acid, as in the Feulgen procedure, an extra hydroxy group is liberated on C_1 by the removal of the purine moiety from the nucleic acid. Consequently if there is also a free hydroxyl group on C_2, the compound now contains an α,β-glycol group which should be susceptible to oxidation by periodate. In the case of the thymonucleic acid C_2 does not bear an hydroxyl group, unlike pentose nucleic acid. It is not at present known, however, whether the hydroxy group at C_2 is normally phosphorylated in pentose nucleic acid. If it is not, after a Feulgen-type hydrolysis, pentose nucleic acid should contain a glycol grouping which can react with periodate.

An attempt has been made to study the distribution of a substance with the above structure in tissues, using the following procedures:

1. The tissue is embedded in wax, one result of which is to remove any fatty aldehyde which may be present.
2. It is necessary to remove any preformed glycol grouping. This is quite readily done by treatment with periodate which transforms the glycol groups into aldehyde groupings. These groups are later (in Step 4) blocked with hydroxylamine or dimedone.
3. Sections are submitted to a Feulgen hydrolysis in the presence of mercury. The hydrolysis splits off purine. The mercury prevents nucleic acid from going into solution.
4. As a result of the Feulgen hydrolysis reactive aldehyde groups are liberated on the deoxy sugars but not on the normal sugars. This reactive aldehyde, together with that formed in Step 2, is blocked by treatment with hydroxylamine or dimedone.
5. The sections are then treated with periodate to oxidize any α,β-glycols liberated in Step 3 to aldehyde groups.
6. The section is exposed to reduced fuchsin to colour the sites of aldehyde groups.

When this procedure is carried out it has been found that with a number of tissues, e.g., pancreas, a colour appears in those sites in the cytoplasm and nucleus which are believed to contain pentose nucleic acid. This investigation, however, has been made in only a very preliminary way, and it by no means follows that the colour which is developed under those conditions is necessarily due to pentose nucleic acid. All that can be said is that the procedure which is given has demonstrated the presence of a substance, which is normally masked in tissues, but which is brought into a form which will react with periodate by a Feulgen-type hydrolysis.

Procedures of the type which have just been outlined will permit the detection of a considerable variety of substances. Treatment of a tissue with periodate followed by reduced fuchsin will demonstrate the presence of α,β-glycol groups such as those of glycogen. By using a Feulgen hydrolysis instead of periodate oxidation, deoxynucleic acid may be demonstrated. An oxidation carried out after hydrolysis will demonstrate certain types of masked glycols such as those found in readily hydrolyzed glycosides. It is also possible that a good deal of evidence can be collected about the orientation of the hydroxyl groups in these glycols. For example, the *cis* glycols can probably be prevented from reacting with periodate by formation of the acetonyl compounds, or, as Seymour Cohen has suggested to me, perhaps by the use of borate in the periodate mixture. *Trans* hydroxy groups do not readily form acetonyl compounds, nor do they have the property, possessed by *cis* compounds, of forming a complex with borate. Neither the acetonyl compound nor the complex with borate is likely to react with periodate.

By using procedures of this type it should be possible to obtain very useful information about many of the natural polysaccharides, including the polysaccharides present in the mucoproteins and intracellular matrixes.

REFERENCES

BENNET. 1940. *Am. J. Anat., 67,* 151.
BOSCOT, MANDL, DANIELLI, AND SHOPPEE. 1948. *Nature, 162,* 572.
CAIN. 1949. *Quart. J. Micro. Sci., 90,* 411.
CAMBER. 1949. *Nature, 163,* 285.
DANIELLI. 1949a. *Quart. J. Micro. Sci., 90,* 67.
　　　　1949b. *Quart. J. Micro. Sci., 90,* 309.
　　　　1950. *Quart. J. Micro. Sci., 91,* 215.

DEMPSEY et al. 1943. *Endocrin., 33,* 387.

1944. *Endocrin., 35,* 409.

FEULGEN AND ROSSENBECK. 1924. *Zeit. Physiol. Chem., 135,* 203.

FEULGEN AND VOIGT. 1924. *Pflügers Arch., 206,* 389.

HOTCHKISS. 1948. *Arch. Biochem., 16,* 131.

LEHNINGER. 1945. *J. Biol. Chem., 161,* 415.

STEDMAN AND STEDMAN. 1943. *Nature, 157,* 740.

WORDEN. 1943. *Nature, 152,* 505.

CHAPTER 5

THE CYTOCHEMISTRY OF PROTEINS AND NUCLEIC ACIDS

Introduction

A common characteristic of the proteins and the nucleic acids is that they both normally occur as macromolecules. It is, of course, desirable if possible to characterize macromolecules by their properties as a whole. But this is usually impossible, particularly in cytochemistry, and it is usually only by studying the reactivity of certain chemical groups present in the macromolecules that these substances are identified. Consequently, there is much similarity in the methods which are employed in the study of the various proteins and nucleic acids, and in the difficulties which are encountered in these studies. A convenient classification of the groups present in proteins and nucleic acids which are available for study from the cytochemical point of view is:

1. Carbohydrate groups. These may be found both in nucleic acids and in proteins. Part of the cytochemistry of these groups has been discussed in Chapter 4.

2. Phosphate groups. Until recently phosphate groups have mainly been studied in relation to nucleic acid. It is known, however, that in addition to the phospho-proteins of yolk and of milk, other phosphoproteins occur in nature. Myosin, for example, is probably a phosphorylated protein.

3. Resonating ring structures. These are groups such as purines, pyrimidines, tryptophane, tyrosine, and haem. These groups have the capacity for absorbing light vigorously. Most of the naturally occurring resonating ring groups of proteins and nucleic acids absorb in the ultraviolet region, but a few, such as haem, also absorb light in the visible spectrum.

4. Peptide linkages. These are found in proteins only, so far as is known.

5. Reactive side-groups. These include such groups as NH_2, CO_2H, SH, OH, tyrosine, histidine, tryptophane, etc.

6. Enzyme activity. One method of characterizing a protein molecule as a whole is by its enzyme activity. The study of alkaline phosphatase discussed in Chapter 3 is, of course, an example of this.

7. Antigens. It is probable that individual proteins can conveniently be studied by their reaction with coloured antibodies.

The number of methods available for study of the nucleic acids and the proteins is considerable, although as yet far from sufficient for obtaining all the information which is required about their cytochemistry. The methods include:

1. Observation of the intrinsic absorption spectrum.
2. Observations made after the use of chromogenic reagents which react with particular groups.
3. Determination of the localization of enzyme activity.
4. Observation of the reactions of tissues with colored antibodies.
5. Staining with dyes.
6. Study of the action of enzymes such as proteolytic enzymes and nucleases, on tissue sections and squashes, etc.

In this chapter we shall consider only the methods involved in 1, 2, and 4. The methods concerned in 3 have already been considered in Chapter 3. The methods involved in 5 and 6 are, in my view, not sufficiently reliable except for preliminary studies. The reasons for this have been given elsewhere (Danielli, 1946), and there seems to be no reason for revising the opinions given in this earlier publication.

The Analysis of Intrinsic Absorption Spectra

As has been shown by the accomplished work of Caspersson and his school, a remarkable amount of information about proteins and nucleic acids can be obtained even when one is limited to studying the ultraviolet absorption spectra. When reflecting microscopes become more readily available it should be possible to use, with more or less equal facility, absorption bands ranging from the infrared to the far ultraviolet. At present most studies have been limited to the regions between 2500 A.U. and 3000 A.U., which is the region in which the pyrimidine ring and some of the groups of proteins have strong absorption bands. It is unlikely that the extreme ultraviolet beyond 2400 will be a very profitable region for study, since so many substances have strong absorption bands in this region. There is also a considerable limitation on the usefulness of moving into the infrared regions, due to the decline in resolving power as one moves into the longer wavelength regions of the spectrum. This limitation is more severe than is generally realized. Thus, although the limit of resolution is given by $\lambda/2$, it is necessary to have a region at least 3 λ in diameter before quantitative studies of its absorption spectrum can be made. Thus, if one is employing light with a wavelength of 4 μ, whilst the resolution limit is 2 μ, the size of area which is needed for studying the absorption spectrum for light of wavelength 4 μ is at least 12 μ. Thus studies in this region of the infrared would only be useful with very large cells.

The characteristic absorbing unit of the nucleic acids is the pyrimidine ring, found in both the pyrimidines and in the purines. In nucleic acids these rings produce a very strong absorption of light in the region of 2600 A.U. The exact position of the absorption band of individual purines and pyrimidines varies, according to the side-groups which are present on the ring structure. Thus a considerable change in position of the absorption bands may occur when an NH_2 group is replaced by an OH group. Until now observations on the nucleic acids have been limited to those which can be made without modification of the purine and pyrimidine rings. But it may quite well be possible to modify the absorption spectrum by carrying out reactions with these ring structures.

In the proteins the main absorbing components are tryptophane and tyrosine, which absorb strongly in the region of 2800 A.U. The absorption of light by tyrosine is sensitive to pH changes. The remaining amino acids absorb light rather strongly in the region of 2400 A.U.

Generally speaking, it is probably true that one can determine the amount of the nucleic acid and of protein by making observations at a number of different wavelengths in the ultraviolet. It must, however, be remembered that the absorption of light is a property not of a molecule as a whole, but of some of the smaller constituent groups. It is not impossible for some of the purines and pyrimidines occurring in nucleic acids to occur as constituent groups of proteins, and for some of the amino acids to occur as constituent groups of nucleic acids. Panijel has found a protein in *Ascaris* sperm which contains purine but no phosphorus. Thus although this protein has an absorption spectrum similar to nucleo-protein since it lacks phosphorus it cannot contain nucleic acid.

Very few studies have been made in the visible region of the spectrum, since most proteins do not absorb light to a significant degree in the visible. An exception to this is the very interesting study which Thorell (1947) has made of the formation of hemoglobin during the development of red blood cells.

A typical example of the work of Caspersson is illustrated by Fig. 5.

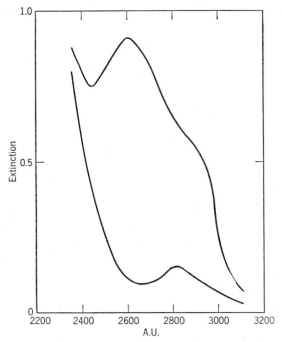

FIG. 5. Extinction coefficients for a point on a chromosome (upper curve) and in the cytoplasm (lower curve) of a *Tradescantia* pollen mother cell. The absorption at 2800 A.U. is mainly caused by protein, and at 2600 A.U., mainly by nucleic acid. After Caspersson, 1950, page 66.

General Principles Involved in the Use of Chromogenic Reagents

There are a wide variety of agents which may be used in order to produce an absorption of light by proteins or nucleic acids in various parts of the spectrum. Up to the present these agents have been almost entirely restricted to the development of absorption bands in the visible region of the spectrum. It seems likely that in the future attempts will be made to use reagents producing absorption in the ultraviolet and infrared regions. But with all regions of the spectrum, the same general problems must be taken into consideration. The general requirements of a chromogenic reagent are:

1. The reagent should not give a generalized staining, i.e., it shall be inert to most components of a tissue section and also it should be colourless itself.

2. The reagent should be readily washed out of sections by inert solvents.

3. The reagent should have a known specificity, i.e., it must be known just what groups it will attack.

4. The product of the reaction between the agent and the protein or nucleic acid shall be indiffusible.

5. The reagent shall produce its effect under mild conditions. For example, it is essential that none of the steps involved shall dissolve components of the tissue section.

6. It is desirable that there should be several independent methods for colouring the same group, so that the results obtained by these different methods may be compared.

Many of the points concerned have been discussed in more detail elsewhere (Danielli, 1946–1949).

Practically all the chemical reagents which are available will in fact attack more than one group of a protein or nucleic acid. Consequently, it is frequently necessary to use two reagents, one of which will be a non-chromogenic reagent used to block one of the groups which would otherwise be coloured by the other reagent. In fact, it can safely be said that the development of non-chromogenic blocking agents is a key point in the cytochemistry of the proteins.

The complication which has not as yet received consideration is the accessibility of some of the chemical groups of proteins and nucleic acids to the reagent being used. It is well known from the work of Anson and Mirsky and others that tyrosine and SH groups of proteins may be masked in a native protein, and only become accessible to chemical reagents after denaturation. Similar observations have been made on histidine, and no doubt all groups of proteins are to some extent inaccessible to chemical reagents. Sometimes, as is the case with histidine, a group which is accessible to a reagent in a native protein may become inaccessible in a denatured one. This question of masked groups presents a very difficult problem for cytochemistry, particularly in

view of the fact that a considerable part of the protein in a fixed
tissue section is in the denatured state. I shall not dwell on this
point further at the present time. But it should perhaps be mentioned that this problem does not really become important in
most cases until quantitative studies are being made. At present
there is so much doubt as to how far microspectrophotometric
observations are quantitative that it does not seem worth while
to go into the problems arising from masking and unmasking of
chemical groupings.

DIAZONIUM HYDROXIDES AS CHROMOGENIC REAGENTS

Diazonium hydroxides will react with histidine, tryptophane,
and possibly nucleic acid to give azo dyes. There are, of course,
many other possible components of tissues with which diazonium
hydroxides will react, including most phenols. The most convenient diazonium hydroxides have so far proved to be tetrazotised benzidine and dianisidine. Frequently it is found that, when
one of these compounds is allowed to react with a tissue section,
a sufficient intensity of colour is developed for cytochemical purposes. Under these conditions the reagent is linked onto the protein or nucleic acid by only one of its two active groups. If, however, the colour is not sufficiently intense, it may be intensified
by washing the section to free it from excess of reagent, and
then placing the section in a solution of phenol or amine which
then couples onto the free end of the reagent. For example,*

* Here and elsewhere, Pr denotes protein.

A typical procedure would be as follows:

1. A piece of tissue is submitted to freeze-drying and sectioned after embedding in wax.

2. After removal of the wax and passing through alcohol the sections are placed for 10 minutes in a solution of 0.2 percent tetrazotised benzidine at about 4° C., in sodium veronal buffer.

3. The sections are then washed for 1 minute in each of three changes of 0.1 N hydrochloric acid. It is essential that this washing should be very thorough, and the solutions must be changed frequently to secure this.

4. The sections are then placed for 15 minutes in a suspension of 0.1 gram of α- or β-naphthol suspended in sodium bicarbonate or sodium veronal solution.

5. The sections are washed in distilled water and mounted in balsam.

Since the diazonium hydroxides can react with a number of tissue components, it is usually necessary to use blocking agents to prevent the chromogenic reagent from combining with all the groups which are open to attack. Among suitable reagents for blocking purposes are dinitrofluorobenzene, performic acid, and benzoyl chloride. Dinitrofluorobenzene will block all phenols and also histidine; performic acid destroys tryptophane; and benzoyl chloride destroys histidine, tryptophane, and tyrosine. Some of the possible permutations and combinations of blocking agents are shown in Table VII.

TABLE VII

The ability of certain amino acid residues to react with diazonium hydroxides after treatment with various reagents.

Reagent	None	2:4 Dinitro Fluoroben- zene	Performic Acid	Benzoyl Chloride
Histidine	+	?	+	−
Tryptophane	+	+	−	−
Tyrosine	+	−	+	−

The use of diazonium hydroxides for the study of nucleic acids was first suggested by J. S. Mitchell. He suggested that a tissue section should first be subjected to benzoylation and then exposed to a diazonium hydroxide. The reactive amino acids would be destroyed by benzoylation, and only the nucleic acids should be free to react. Mitchell's conditions of benzoylation were unsatisfactory. He used benzoyl chloride in sodium hydroxide solution: under these conditions the reaction with benzoyl chloride is patchy, and also the sodium hydroxide extracts much material from the sections. I have found that a much more reliable technique is to use a 5 percent solution of benzoyl chloride in dry pyridine, for about 12 hours.

There is also some doubt as to whether nucleic acid can, in fact, react with diazonium hydroxides under the circumstances suggested by Mitchell. It is certainly true, however, that after benzoylation, treatment with a diazonium hyroxide produces a distribution of colour which is very similar to the distribution of nucleic acid revealed by other processes. Further inquiry into the chemistry of this reaction is clearly necessary.

NITRO COMPOUNDS AS CHROMOGENIC REAGENTS

There are many nitro compounds in use in organic chemistry as analytical reagents. Many of these will react with nucleic acids and proteins. Some of these substances give a reaction product which is coloured. Thus, according to Sanger, dinitrofluorobenzene will react with tyrosine, histidine, NH_2 groups, and SH groups. Of these, the reaction products with histidine, NH_2 groups, and SH groups are coloured. Usually, however, the intensity of colour is too low to be satisfactory for cytochemical problems. The intensity of the colour may be increased to a satisfactory degree by reduction of the nitro group of the reagent to an amino group, diazotisation of the resulting amino group, followed by linkage to a phenol or amine. This procedure produces an azo dye, which is linked by covalent bonds to the group which is being studied. A typical reaction is the following:

$$Pr \cdot NH_2 \rightarrow Pr \cdot NH \left\langle \begin{array}{c} NO_2 \\ \\ \end{array} \right\rangle NO_2 \rightarrow Pr \cdot NH \left\langle \begin{array}{c} NO_2 \\ \\ \end{array} \right\rangle NH_2$$

$$\downarrow$$

$$\leftarrow Pr \cdot NH \left\langle \begin{array}{c} NO_2 \\ \\ \end{array} \right\rangle N{=}N \cdot OH$$

$$Pr \cdot NH \left\langle \begin{array}{c} NO_2 \\ \\ \end{array} \right\rangle N{=}N \left\langle \begin{array}{c} \\ \\ \end{array} \right\rangle NH_2$$

The details of the procedure necessary for using some of these nitro compounds have been worked out together with L. G. Bell and A. Loveless. The basic procedure is as follows:

1. Sections are placed for 1 hour in a suspension of 0.5 milliliter of dinitrofluorobenzene and 1 gram of sodium bicarbonate in 100 milliliters of 70 percent alcohol. Under these conditions linkage of the dinitrofluorobenzene to tyrosine, histidine, NH_2 groups, and SH groups may occur.

2. The sections are washed in three changes of 70 percent alcohol, 5 minutes in each change, to remove uncombined dinitrofluorobenzene.

3. The sections are then treated for 2 minutes with a solution of chromous chloride in 0.1 N hydrochloric acid. This reduces the nitro groups of the dinitrofluorobenzene which is linked to various groups in the section (i.e., $R \cdot NO_2 \rightarrow R \cdot NH_2$).

TABLE VIII

Some nitro reagents, and groups for the localization of which these reagents may be particularly useful.

	Tyro-sine	SH	NH₂	CO₂H	CHOH
NO_2-⟨⟩-NO_2 (F)	+	+	+		
NO_2-⟨⟩-NCO	+	+	+		
NO_2-⟨⟩-CH_2Br				+	
NH_2-⟨⟩-AsO		+			
NO_2-⟨⟩-$NH \cdot CO \cdot CH_2I$		+	+		
NO_2-⟨⟩-$O \cdot CO \cdot CH_2I$		+			
NO_2-⟨⟩-$COCl$					+

4. Sections are washed in two changes of 0.1 N hydrochloric acid for 3 or 4 minutes, and transferred to

5. A nitrous acid solution obtained by dissolving 0.5 gram of sodium nitrite in 100 milliliters 0.1 N hydrochloric acid kept at 0° C. The sections are kept in this solution for 5 minutes to diazotise the amino groups.

6. The sections are transferred to an alkaline solution of a phenol or a solution of an aromatic amine, e.g., H acid or α-naphthol or β-naphthylamine. After 15 minutes in this solution coupling with the diazotised sections should be complete.

7. The sections are washed in tap water and mounted in balsam.

Table VIII gives a list of some of the nitro reagents which are usually available and indicates the groups of proteins for the study of which they are particularly suitable.

ALDEHYDES AS CHROMOGENC REAGENTS

A third family of compounds useful in the cytochemistry of proteins are those containing two reactive groups, one of which is an aldehyde group and the other of which may be any of a

TABLE IX

Aldehyde reagents under investigation for the cytochemistry of —SH and —NH₂ groups.

	NH₂	SH
CHO⬡CHO	+	
CHO⬡NH₂	+	
CHO⬡NO₂	+	
CHO⬡COCH₂Br		+
CHO⬡O·CO·CH₂I		+
CHO⬡NH·CO·CH₂I		+

considerable variety of groups. Table IX shows the formulae for a number of these reagents. These are being investigated in collaboration with A. Loveless and L. G. Bell. The reagents may be used in two ways. Thus the CHO group may be allowed to react with the NH_2 groups of a protein. After this reaction has gone to completion, the second reactive group (e.g., NO_2 or NH_2) may be subjected to the procedure discussed in the previous section, to produce a colour. In other cases, the second reactive group is allowed to react with the protein, the CHO group being kept intact. The section is then exposed to reduced fuchsin, which forms a purple colour with the aldehyde group. The following is an example of this type of reaction:

$$Pr \cdot NH_2 + CHO \langle \bigcirc \rangle NH_2 \rightarrow Pr \cdot NH \cdot CHOH \langle \bigcirc \rangle NH_2$$

$$\downarrow$$

$$\leftarrow Pr \cdot NH \cdot CHOH \langle \bigcirc \rangle N = N \cdot OH$$

$$Pr = NH \cdot CHOH \langle \bigcirc \rangle N = N \langle \bigcirc \rangle NH_2$$

BLOCKING AGENTS

As was pointed out above, chromogenic reagents are usually able to react with several of the groups found in a tissue section. Consequently, before the results obtained with a chromogenic reagent can be analyzed, it is necessary to make studies on sections in which some of the reactive groups have been blocked with non-chromogenic reagents. Table X shows a list of such reagents and of the groups which they can conveniently be used to block.

Some of the reagents given in Table X are able potentially to react with a considerable number of the chemical groups of a protein. But the actual range of their blocking activity can be restricted by controlling the pH at which the blocking reaction is carried out, and controlling the time of exposure to the blocking agent. This is the case, for example, with phenyl isocyanate and diazonium hydroxides. Some of the blocking reagents have the useful property of having a reversible action. This is the case with Hg, $ClCH_2 \cdot O \cdot CH_3$, PhSCOCl, $ClCH_2 \cdot O \cdot CH = CH_2$, PhAsO, PhHgOH. With these reversible reagents it

TABLE X

Reagents which may be used for blocking various groups in protein molecules. Reagents which may readily be removed are marked with an asterisk.

	Tryptophane	Tyrosine	Histidine	SH	S—S	NH$_2$	CO$_2$H	CHOH
NO$_2$ F⟨⟩NO$_2$		+	?	+		+		
HNO$_2$						+		
HCO·OOH	+			+	+			
⟨⟩COCl	+	+	+	+		+		+
Hg*				+				
ICH$_2$·CONH$_2$				+		?		
⟨⟩COCH$_2$Cl				+				
Glyoxal						+		
Ketene		(+)		+		+		
⟨⟩NCO		+		+		+		
ClCH$_2$·O·CH$_3$*							+	
⟨⟩S·COCl*						+		
Naphthoquinone				+		+		
Methylnaphthoquinone				+				
ClCH$_2$·O·CH=CH$_2$*						+		
⟨⟩AsO*				+				
⟨⟩HgOH*				+				
NO$_2$⟨⟩N=NOH	+	+	+					

is often possible to block a group, carry out a cytochemical procedure, and then remove the blocking agent by a mild treatment with dilute acid, dilute alkali, dithioglycerol, or a heavy metal. After removal of the blocking agent a further cytochemical procedure may be carried out with the group which has been liberated. Thus, for example, NH$_2$ groups may be protected by treatment with PhSCOCl against a reagent for tyrosine. Then treatment with a solution of heavy metal will liberate the NH_2 group which may then be treated with a second cytochemical reagent. A more detailed discussion of these reagents has been given elsewhere (Danielli, 1949).

METHODS OF INCREASING SENSITIVITY

Where tissue components are present in small amounts, the methods given above may not be sufficiently sensitive. So far we have considered three methods for increasing sensitivity.

1. Probably the method which is potentially able to give the greatest increase in sensitivity is to modify procedures of the type given in preceding sections so as to obtain a fluorescent compound. The specimens may then be studied in the fluorescent microscope. A considerable gain in sensitivity should be achieved even by visual inspection. If photographic means are used there should be, in theory, a very great increase in sensitivity indeed. On the other hand, the intrinsic fluorescence of the specimen may pose some difficulties. These, however, may perhaps be met by using selective quenching agents and by observing the fluorescence only in selected regions of the spectrum. Imperfections in the optical equipment will, of course, also set a limit to the sensitivity as determined by photographic methods. We have not as yet paid much attention to the use of fluorescent compounds, but it does hold much promise.

2. A technique which we have found of considerable value involves only a slight modification in many of the procedures set out above. In these procedures colour has been obtained by forming an azo dye in the section. If, in the final stage of the formation of this dye, an amine is used which can be diazotised after coupling, it is in theory possible to repeat the procedure, linking on yet another amine, after diazotisation. Theoretically, this process may be repeated an indefinite number of times. In practice, however, although there is a very considerable increase in the intensity of coloration produced by repeating this step a small number of times, the increase is not directly proportional to the number of couplings, the increment diminishing as the number of couplings is increased. Consequently, we have found, with an amine such as α-naphthylamine, that eight couplings are the maximum which it is profitable to undertake.

3. Another procedure which we have under investigation is to link a sugar onto the compound which is being coloured. To secure this coupling it is necessary to have a sugar or related compound which has been linked with a phenol or an amine in such a way that the resultant compound is competent to react with a diazonium hydroxide. Thus the actual mode of operation is to produce a diazonium hydroxide in the section, possibly a diazotised azo dye as suggested in method 2, and then to couple on the sugar compound just mentioned. When the coupling is completed the sugar may be oxidised with periodic acid. This will give aldehyde groups where previously there were α,β-glycol groups. The aldehyde groups are then treated with reduced fuchsin, which, of course, gives a vigorous colouration. We are at present experimenting in this way with a derivative of inulin. The use of such a polysaccharide is, however, complicated by steric factors, and to what extent the use of such compounds will prove satisfactory cannot at present be predicted.

THE DETECTION OF DIFFUSION ARTEFACTS

All the methods for the study of proteins and nucleic acids which have been discussed have involved the formation of dyes in the sections which are attached by stable covalent bondings to the compound which is to be identified. Consequently, there are no problems arising from the actual diffusion of the dye itself, or from the adsorption of the dye by other compounds in the section. All the methods are so designed that each individual reagent is a small colourless compound, the excess of which can be washed out of the tissue section with comparative ease. Consequently, there should be little trouble arising from unwanted colour produced by residual amounts of reagents. The most serious type of diffusion artefact which is likely to arise under these circumstances is that due to diffusion of the protein or nucleic acid element itself. There is a very serious possibility that such diffusion may occur despite all that can be done in the way of fixation. To detect artefacts of this nature, three methods are in use.

1. To test for the loss of appreciable amounts of components by diffusion, about 0.2 gram of sections is suspended in the various reagents. Each step in the procedure is then carried out on

this considerable quantity of suspended sections, after which the sections are centrifuged down and the fluid phase then tested for protein and nucleic acid. In this way the gross loss of material from sections by diffusion may be detected.

2. Where the components of the tissue which are being stained can be obtained in a soluble condition, a very useful method is to carry out the cytochemical reaction with this solution of the components. Then a tissue section is exposed to the coloured soluble component to see whether it adsorbs upon the section. This reveals the sites of affinity within the section for the coloured component. In cases where the distribution of sites of affinity coincides with distribution of sites of the compound as revealed by a cytochemical method, further enquiry is clearly indicated.

3. Perhaps the most useful method of all is the use of superimposed sections, somewhat along the lines used in the case of alkaline phosphatase. Let us consider as an example the distribution of tyrosine in a section. A section is placed on a slide and treated with a blocking agent so that no residual tyrosine groups remain in it. Then upon this is placed the section which is to be examined, and the cytochemical reaction is carried out with the superimposed sections. If any diffusion artefact occurs, it should be revealed by the appearance of colour for tyrosine in the underlying blocked section.

METHODS FOR THE ELECTRON MICROSCOPE

In 1948 Mr. Walker and Miss Hanson, of Professor Randall's Biophysics Research Unit at King's College, London, asked me whether it would be possible to develop methods of the types discussed above for use with the electron microscope. The physical problem involved is markedly different from that encountered with the light microscope. In the light microscope perception of an object is based upon non-transmission of light as a result either of scattering or absorption, or both. If scattering is reduced to a minimum, and the component which it is wished to observe has an absorption spectrum markedly different from that of any other component present, quite accurate estimations may be made even of small absorptions of light. For example, an absorption of 5 percent of the light passing through an object may be made with an accuracy of better than 10 percent. On the other hand, with electron microscopes, at least as at present conceived, perception is based entirely upon the scattering of electrons. Scattering is a function of the atomic number of the atoms in the material upon which the electron beam impinges. In biological objects, the great bulk of the scattering material is carbon, oxygen, and nitrogen, which differ relatively little in scattering power. Consequently, the image obtained in an electron microscope depends almost entirely upon the mass of material present in different parts of the specimen, and there is little prospect of perceiving chemical differences between different parts of a specimen. Furthermore, the application of reagents to the specimen will facilitate the perception of chemical differences only so far as the reagent adds selectively to the effective electron-scattering power of individual chemical components.

Thus the sensitivity of methods for use in the electron microscope is limited by the sensitivity of the instrument to differences in scattering power. With the techniques available at the moment, it appears that, to obtain reproducible results, the scattering power of a component must be altered by at least 10 percent. To increase the scattering power by this amount is difficult, compared with the small changes in chemical composition which will give a significant change in the transmission of visible light. Consequently, one cannot expect, without marked improvement in the instruments available, to obtain methods of the same degree of sensitivity as those available for the light microscope. On the other hand, the great advantage in resolving power possessed by the electron microscope justifies the development of even crude cytochemical methods. In this direction we have had some success. The work has been carried out in the main by Mr. Stuart-Webb and Mr. Bell of my department, and Dr. Bovet and Dr. Lamb of Professor Randall's department.

After some search for a suitable test object, it was found that thin gelatin films could be obtained which were sufficiently uniform in thickness for preliminary investigations. With these thin films the following procedure was worked out, in which the scattering power of components which will react with dinitrofluorobenzene is markedly increased, partly by combination with a large organic group, and partly by subsequent linkage with a heavy metal.

1. Reaction with dinitrofluorobenzene.
2. Reduction of the nitro groups to NH_2 with chromous sulfate.
3. Diazotisation of the NH_2 groups.
4. Combination with K acid or dithiol.
5. Combination with silver or lead.

This technique was applied to spermatozoa. The mean opacity of the middle piece of bull spermatozoa, before treatment, was 0.825. After the treatment via K acid and silver the opacity was increased to 1.21, and after the treatment via dithiol and lead the scattering power was 1.20. From these increases it was calculated that between 8 percent and 14 percent of the middle piece consisted of material able to react with dinitrofluorobenzene.

Potentially, most of the methods outlined above could be modified for use in the electron microscope. But there are many difficulties to be overcome, from the points of view of technique of staining, of interpretation, and of accuracy of estimating scattering power.

The Systems Concerned in Protein Synthesis

At the date of writing the main contribution, from the cyto-chemical point of view, to our knowledge of the systems concerned in protein synthesis has come from the laboratory of T. Caspersson in Stockholm. These contributions have been published in a series of papers commencing in 1932, and have been summarised in a recent monograph entitled *Cell Growth and Cell Function* (1950). Probably the most important of these contributions has been the observation of the constant association of nucleic acids with protein formation. In his monograph Caspersson recapitulates the generalization made by Caspersson and Schultz, based on the study of nuclei, bacteria, viruses, etc., "that all self-reproducing protein molecules need the cooperation of nucleic acids for reproduction" (p. 100). Caspersson also states that "the nucleic acids take part in the processes leading to the synthesis of cellular proteins, not only in the nucleus but also in the cytoplasm" (p. 140). These views have illumined many previous observations and have inspired a remarkable volume of work by other investigators in a wide variety of fields.

In pursuing the further analysis of the association of protein synthesis and nucleic acids, there are three important questions which will be considered here. These are:

1. Do nucleic acids participate chemically in protein synthesis? Alternatively,
2. Are nucleic acids essential chemical or physical components of the environment in which protein synthesis occurs?
3. What are the sites of protein synthesis?

To obtain a satisfactory answer to question 1 is by no means simple. For example, if the nucleic acids had catalytic functions, it is unlikely that chemical changes in the nucleic acid during protein synthesis could be detected even by the use of isotopes. On the other hand, if the phosphate groups of nucleic acids participated in protein synthesis, it is likely that a phosphorus turnover could be detected by isotopic studies.

Question 2 is also by no means simple, for there are many conceivable functions of nucleic acids which fall within the framework of this question. Two examples of these may be considered as illustrations. One much publicised theory has been that the nucleic acids serve as templates or moulds, upon which the protein is formed. So far as this theory implies that the surface of a nucleic acid molecule can determine the sequence of amino acids in a polypeptide chain, it seems to me quite naive, from a physico-chemical point of view. To the extent to which the template function is limited to determining the manner in which a polypeptide chain is folded into a unique configuration there is more to be said for this theory. A quite different alternative theory is that the nucleic acids constitute a necessary part of the environment in the same way that water does. Water is an essential for protein synthesis, acting as a solvent, as part of the protein structure, and possibly also as a catalyst and even as a direct participant in the synthetic process; nucleic acid could, so far as present knowledge goes, have a similarly essential role as an environmental factor.

The third question engenders a different set of enquiries. The simplest approach to this problem is to suppose that the places in cells which have the highest concentrations of protein are the sites of synthesis. The intrinsic fallacy in accepting such a hypothesis without proof may readily be seen if we consider the somewhat broader scene of protein production in a countryside: the highest concentrations of protein are to be found in the slaughterhouses, cold-storage centres, and granaries, but the actual sites of synthesis are the fields, pastures, and woodlands, in which protein may be said, both literally and figuratively, to be thin on the ground. Consequently, although it is of much interest to discover and record the sites of occurrence of proteins in cells, we must refrain from identifying the richer sites with sites of synthesis until proof of this identity is obtained.

With these considerations in mind, we may now proceed to examine the problem in more detail.

CASPERSSON'S CYTOLOGICAL SYSTEMS

First consider the observations connected with chromosome reproduction. It was shown by studies on chromosomes, particularly those of grasshopper spermatocytes, that the chromosomes are richer in nucleic acid during nuclear division than at any other time. This was interpreted as indicating "a connection between the duplication of the genes and the presence of nucleic acid."

Taking the salivary gland nucleus of Drosophila as typical of an intermitotic nucleus, Caspersson advances the view that the euchromatic * regions of a chromosome produce proteins which are rich in tryptophane and tyrosine, whereas the heterochromatic regions produce proteins which are rich in diamino acids.

Then, turning to reproduction of cytoplasmic protein, Caspersson believes that the process commences by formation of nucleolar protein within a chromocentre. Thus the chromocentre becomes distended and the Feulgen-positive material appears as a ring, halo, or crescent contiguous with the newly formed nucleolus. The chromocentre in this condition is commonly called the "nucleolus-associated chromatin." There is a very great volume of evidence to indicate that the nucleolus is intimately connected with formation of cytoplasmic protein. So far as is known there are few, if any, exceptions to the rule that cells which are rapidly forming cytoplasmic protein have prominent nucleoli. During the formation of ova in the ovary, in which very large quantities of cytoplasmic protein are formed, one or more nucleoli are usually by far the most striking feature of the nucleus. In developing eggs, nucleoli are far from prominent during the early cleavage phases, which appear to be primarily concerned with securing distributions of the original yolk material and the establishment of the early differentiation pattern. But after this new antigens, i.e., new proteins, appear in the embryo; during this phase the nucleoli become prominent.

According to Caspersson, the nucleolar material is rich in diamino acids. Although the nucleolus itself is lacking in deoxy nucleic acid, it may absorb light strongly in the region of 2600 A.U. and is then supposed to be rich in pentose nucleic acid. The content of pentose nucleic acid is, however, very variable.

It was also found that within the nucleus there is a gradient in concentration of the protein rich in diamino-acid from nucleolus to the nuclear membrane. In the cytoplasm there is a high concentration of pentose nucleic acid and of protein adjacent to

---

* Euchromatic regions have a low content of deoxy nucleic acid between mitoses, whereas heterochromatic regions retain much deoxy nucleic acid during the intermitotic phase.

the nuclear membrane, but the concentration diminishes farther away from the nuclear membrane.

From these observations Caspersson concluded that "the nucleic acids take part in the synthesis of cellular proteins, not only in the nucleus but also in the cytoplasm."

CASPERSSON'S CHEMICAL SYSTEM

Corresponding to the pattern of behaviour and composition of the various cell organs just outlined, a scheme of chemical organisation is postulated. The scheme may be summarised under four headings:

1. Nucleic acids participate in an essential manner in the formation of both nuclear and cytoplasmic proteins.

2. In the reproduction of the gene protein, the participating nucleic acids are of the deoxypentose type.

3. In the formation of the cytoplasmic proteins, the participating nucleic acids are of the pentose type.

4. The nucleolus-associated chromatin (or heterochromatin) governs the level of nucleic acid formation, and consequently also determines the rate of protein production.

These four postulates all derive ultimately from the experimentally observed correlation between protein synthesis and the existence of a high concentration of nucleic acids within the same cell. This correlation is quite adequately established. But, on the other hand, there are other ingredients in these four postulates which are not so well established and need more critical examination. To conduct this examination, and to obtain more precise information about the manner in which nucleic acids control protein production, we can profitably consider a number of studies made by other than cytochemical methods. But before doing so it is desirable to consider briefly the nature of the systems in which the nucleic acid-protein synthesis has been securely established.

SYSTEMS DISPLAYING PROTEIN SYNTHESIS AND HIGH NUCLEIC ACID CONCENTRATIONS

A very interesting system to study from this point of view is the growing oocyte and its attendant nurse cells, and the subsequent development of the fertilised ovum. In the formation of the oocyte a great increase in cytoplasmic protein occurs with very little reproduction of genes. During this period the deoxy nucleic acids of the oocyte nucleus are scanty in amount, relative to the size of the cell, whereas pentose nucleic acids are plentiful in the cytoplasm both of the oocyte and of the nurse cells, as has been shown by Brachet. When the oocyte has reached its maximum size, the cytoplasmic nucleic acid may diminish. After fertilisation there ensues a period of rapid cell division, and therefore of gene synthesis, with little change in cytoplasmic protein: during this period the total nuclear deoxynucleic acid increases rapidly. When the individual organs are forming, the cytoplasm and nuclei are both rich in nucleic acid during the phase of multiplication of cells and of cell growth. But once the organ is established the cytoplasmic nucleic acid may fall sharply and is high only in those cells which produce large amounts of protein, and in these cells only at the time of protein production. All these observations are consonant with Caspersson's views.

So far as investigation has gone, observations on plant growth fit into the same pattern. In the growing root tip, the cells which are multiplying rapidly are much richer in deoxynucleic acids than are the other cells. The cells in which cytoplasmic protein is being formed rapidly are rich in pentose nucleic acids, whereas those cells which are not producing protein may be almost devoid of the pentose acids. In yeasts and bacteria the situation is the same: high protein production is associated with a high concentration of pentose nucleic acids, whereas resting phases contain little pentose nucleic acid.

Rapidly growing tumours have cells whose cytoplasm is rich in pentose nucleic acids; under the action of growth-restricting treatment, the cytoplasmic nucleic acid falls rapidly.

When the different cells composing a protein-secreting organ are examined, the same pattern emerges. Those cells which are vigorously secreting protein are rich in nucleic acid, and the remainder are not. Thus the exocrine cells of the pancreas are rich, the endocrine cells are poor. In the gastric mucosa the HCl-secreting cells are poor in nucleic acids, and the protein-secreting cells are rich. Amongst the richest cells of all in pentose nucleic acid are the motor neurons studied by Hyden (1947). When vigorously stimulated, nerve cells may lose two-thirds of their protein: in a subsequent resting phase this protein is rapidly reconstituted. It is thus not surprising to find the neurons so rich in nucleic acid. If, however, the nerve axon is severed there is a marked decline in cytoplasmic nucleic acid, followed by a recovery as regeneration proceeds.

Thus the evidence shows that there is a widespread association between protein production and high nucleic acid contents of cells.

BIOCHEMICAL STUDIES OF PROTEIN SYNTHESIS

E. S. G. Barron has studied protein synthesis in bone marrow, using isotopic phosphorus to detect phosphorus turnover in the nucleic acids. In this system cytoplasmic protein synthesis is very rapid indeed. But there is no detectable turnover of nucleic acid phosphorus.

The reproduction of bacteriophage is another fascinating system. Type T phage growing in *E. coli* contain a large amount of deoxynucleic acids: they may thus be regarded as providing a model experiment in nuclear-protein formation of the type concerned in chromosome reproduction. The facts have been summarized by Seymour Cohen (1949).

In the growth phase, normal *E. coli* produce about three times as much pentose nucleic acid as deoxy nucleic acid. When the bacteria are infected with phage T2r+, nucleic acid formation appears to stop abruptly. Protein synthesis, on the other hand, proceeds rapidly at a linear rate. Then, at approximately 7 minutes after infection, deoxy nucleic acid formation recommences, at a linear rate which is about four times the normal rate of formation. There is no significant formation of pentose nucleic acid. Thus protein formation substantially *precedes* formation of new deoxy nucleic acid. It was shown by Hershey, Kalmunson, and Bronfenbrenner that T2r+ phage does not react with antisera to *E. coli;* consequently, the protein which is formed is not bacterial protein but a new antigen. The time relationships of formation of new protein and nucleic acid after infection are shown in Fig. 6.

From the data obtained with phage it is clear that after infection substantial protein synthesis occurs without the formation of new nucleic acid. It could be concluded that the formation of the specific protein of phage does not involve participation of nucleic acid. But this would hardly be justified, since the infecting phage particles may carry sufficient phage nucleic acid into the bacteria to promote synthesis of a considerable amount of phage protein. Furthermore, there is as yet no evidence that bacterial nucleic acid present before infection does not participate in phage-protein synthesis.

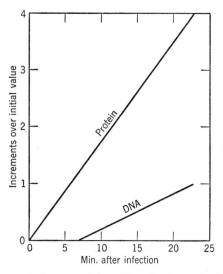

Fɪɢ. 6. Synthesis of deoxy nucleic acid and of protein in *E. coli* after infection by phage.

Further valuable information about the course of phage formation in bacteria has been obtained by the use of radiations. Latarget (1948) studied the effect of X-irradiation of infected cells. For up to 7 minutes after infection the results were characteristic of a system in which it is necessary to secure only one hit per original phage particle to prevent reproduction of that particle. In the period from 9 to 13 minutes after infection it is necessary to record more than one hit per infecting particle to destroy the phage. From 13 minutes after infection until the bursting of the bacteria the actual number of phage particles present does not appear to increase, but the resistance of the particles to irradiation does increase markedly. The rise in resistance may be due to an increase in size of the new virus particles.

Thus from the combination of biochemical and radiation studies it appears that new protein formation markedly precedes new nucleic acid formation. But the formation of new genetically active particles is not complete until new nucleic acid is formed.

Further information may be derived from studies of bacteria which have multiple infection, i.e., more than one phage particle per cell. Lea and Salaman (1946) had concluded that a large phage particle has a zone sensitive to X-rays which is composed of at least 14 distinct units. Luria and Latarget (1947) and Luria (1947), using ultraviolet irradiation, obtained results compatible with the conclusions drawn from the use of X-rays, and showed that there are 30–50 dissociable loci in a phage particle, all of which are necessary for successful reproduction of phage. In cases of multiple infection, reproduction was still possible so long as at least one of each type of locus remained in the cell, i.e., new phage could be produced as a result of some form of collaboration between different loci of separate phage particles in the same cell, although none of the phage particles taken singly in a cell could reproduce.

If it were permissible to generalise from the results on phage to protein production in general, one would be tempted to ask whether protein production is in fact determined by nucleic acid. In the case of phage the evidence, though not definitive, provides a hint that protein production may be independent of nucleic acids, or alternatively that the nucleic acids may be responsible merely for the organisation of synthesized protein, or for some final stage in protein formation other than synthesis of peptide bonds. It also seems certain that nucleic acid phosphorus is not necessarily labile during protein synthesis. But to compare the evidence obtained with phage with cytochemical studies is in any event premature, because of a number of technical weaknesses in the evidence available from cytochemical methods. These weaknesses include:

(a) The fact that little work has been done on the cytochemical changes of individual cells through a cycle of growth and division. Most of the results available have been obtained on fixed material, the cells of which are in different stages of growth. The exact placing of individual cells of a fixed preparation in a sequence corresponding to their growth stages is necessarily somewhat a matter of opinion, and to that extent unsatisfactory.

(b) Most of the work on fixed cells has involved the use of fixatives such as acetic alcohol. As indicated in Chapter 2, such fixation may result in serious diffusion artefacts, and it is hardly profitable to consider results on tissues which have been prepared other than by freeze-drying.

(c) In the interpretation of cytochemical results the data which are available show, at best, only that at certain times in the life of a cell there are high concentrations of proteins and other compounds at certain sites in the cell. There is no information available as to where these compounds come from, where they are synthesized, and often there is little information as to what their ultimate fate is within the cell. Caspersson has built up a fairly elaborate system based on the assumption that all the substances concerned move down their concentration gradients. This, however, is a quite unsatisfactory hypothesis, for at least two reasons. First, it is just as characteristic of living cells that substances should move up, rather than down, concentration gradients. Secondly, there can be no question of the substances *diffusing* down the concentration gradients in the cell: if thermal diffusion were concerned, all the substances in a cell would be uniformly distributed over cells in a few seconds. Thus it is clear that, since no such uniform distribution exists with proteins and nucleic acids, these substances are not free to diffuse, and consequently one cannot tell whether concentration gradients in these substances have any relevance to their future distribution in a cell.

We are thus bound to conclude that, although much recent work, especially that of Caspersson and his school and the studies of phage, is most stimulating and provides much valuable evidence, the fact remains that the sites of synthesis of protein within the cell are as yet unknown, and that the exact relationship of nucleic acids to protein synthesis is also unknown. To emphasize this point I wish to conclude this chapter by bringing forward two quite independent alternative theories of the relationship of nucleic acid to protein synthesis, neither of which involves direct participation of the nucleic acids in the formation of the chemical bonds of peptide chains.

That there is a marked degree of species specificity in the biological action of nucleic acids was clearly demonstrated by the experiments of Avery, McLeod, and McCarty, in which it was shown that type changes in bacteria were mediated only by the action of the nucleic acids of that species. Further evidence was obtained by Mazia, who showed that nucleic acids block the development of fertilised sea-urchin eggs and that the action is markedly dependent upon the species from which the nucleic acid is obtained. Hörstadius, Lorch, and Danielli also injected nucleic acids into sea-urchin eggs, and obtained activation which was to a considerable degree dependent upon the source of the nucleic acid. It is therefore clear that any theory of the role of nucleic acid must provide for a considerable degree of species specificity. This, however, can be done in a variety of ways. Two such mechanisms which will be discussed here are (1) that nucleic acids are folding agents and (2) that nucleic acids are trapping agents.

The first of these theories is based upon the fact that the natural proteins of cells consist not merely of a specific peptide chain but of a peptide chain which is folded into a specific configuration. Treatment of natural proteins with so-called denaturing agents, which cause a loss of this specific configuration, causes a loss of biological activity and even a marked loss of ability to react with antibodies to the original natural protein. Thus the unique configuration of a natural protein is fundamental to its normal action. But these unique configurations cannot be produced without some highly specific mechanism. May it not be that the steric factors in this mechanism are provided by nucleic acids? Astbury has pointed out that the distance between nucleotides in nucleic acids closely corresponds to the distance between peptides in a polypeptide chain, so that a precise adlineation between protein and nucleic acid is possible. If now the mechanical properties of the nucleic acid are such as to facilitate a particular manner of folding, we can picture a process in which a polypeptide adsorbs on a nucleic acid molecule, is folded into a unique configuration by folding of the nucleic acid, and is then shed as a folded globular protein. This, of course, leads to the question, what folds the nucleic acid? The reply to this may well reside in a possibility considered in Chapter 3, namely, that the chromosomes, in their active regions, are constantly folding and unfolding, through the action of phosphate esters upon a phosphatase-contractile protein unit in the chromosome. Thus the complete picture of protein production could involve first synthesis of a polypeptide chain—a process not involving nucleic acid—then the adsorption of the polypeptide onto the nucleic acid of a chromosome, followed by contraction of the chromosome region concerned. The contraction would fold the polypeptide-nucleic acid complex into a configuration partly determined by the nucleic acid, and the folded protein would then be shed from the chromosome. If this were so, it would require that, in many cases at least, the genetically active parts of chromosomes would be nucleic acids. Such a view stands

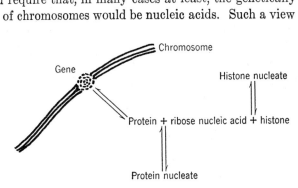

Fig. 7. To illustrate a simple system for protein synthesis, in which pentose nucleic acid is acting as a trapping agent.

in sharp contrast to the theory which regards genes as arrays of enzymes. But it is easy to reconcile such a theory with the species-specific actions of nucleic acids, and with the fact that viruses (which many regard as analogous to genes) appear to have no intrinsic enzymes but do have intrinsic nucleic acids.

The second theory is that nucleic acid is a trapping agent. If, by one means or another, an equilibrium is produced in a cell between a protein and its precursors, then if the protein combines with a trapping agent, which virtually removes it from the system, further protein production must ensue. It is possible that nucleic acids, through their well-known capacity to form complexes with proteins, act as trapping agents. In such a case, during active protein production, it would be necessary to produce nucleic acid in proportion to the amount of protein produced. This leads to a scheme such as that illustrated in Fig. 7 (Danielli, 1949). In this scheme a gene is conceived as a site of protein synthesis and degradation, which is shifted in favour of synthesis by the trapping action of pentose nucleic acid. The equilibrium between protein and pentose nucleic acid is itself controlled by the concentration of histone: since histones are more basic than most proteins, histone will compete for nucleic acid more successfully than most proteins. Hence an increase in histone will cut down protein synthesis, and an increase in pentose nucleic acid will enhance protein synthesis.

The work of Caspersson and Brachet and their colleagues appears to be compatible with this scheme. It is interesting to observe that Stedman and Stedman (1943) found that the concentration of histone is lowest in rapidly growing tissues such as tumours and embryos, as is required by this theory. Correspondingly, in red cells, which have a very high histone content, growth has practically ceased.

If this scheme were correct one would predict that, since protamine is a more basic protein than histone, it should be a more efficient competitor for nucleic acid than is histone, and so should be a strong inhibitor of protein synthesis. That is, synthesis should be very low in cells containing a high protamine content; this is certainly the case with spermatozoa.

We thus have two distinctly possible roles for nucleic acids in protein synthesis, neither of which involves direct participation in formation of polypeptide chains. These two theories seem to me to be equally possible, and the fact that this is so makes it plain that much more information is required. But it must be noted that it is not impossible that both theories may be correct, i.e., that nucleic acids may act both as trapping and as folding agents. One possibility would be that deoxynucleic acid acts mainly as a folding agent, and pentose nucleic acid mainly as a trapping agent.

REFERENCES

Avery, McLeod, and McCarty. 1944. *J. Exp. Med.*, *79*, 137.
Brachet. 1940. *C. r. soc. biol.*, *133*, 90.
Barron. 1949. Personal Communication.
Caspersson. 1947. *Symp. Soc. Exp. Biol.*, *1*, 127.
           1950. *Cell Growth and Cell Function* (Norton, New York).
Caspersson and Schultz. 1938. *Nature*, *122*, 294.
           1939. *Arch. exp. Zellforsch.*, *22*, 650.
Cohen. 1949. *Bact. Rev.*, *13*, 1.
Danielli. 1946a. *Nature*, *157*, 755.
       1946b. *J. Exp. Biol.*, *22*, 110.
       1949. *Cold Spring Harbor Symposia*, *14*, 32.

HERSHEY, KALMUNSON, AND BRONFENBRENNER. 1943. *J. Immunol., 46,* 267.

HÖRSTADIUS, LORCH, AND DANIELLI (unpublished).

HYDEN. 1947. *Symp. Soc. Exp. Biol., 1,* 150.

LATARGET. 1948. *J. Gen. Physiol., 31,* 529.

LEA AND SALAMAN. 1946. *Proc. Roy. Soc., B, 133,* 434.

LURIA. 1947. *Proc. Nat. Acad. Sci. Wash., 33,* 253.

LURIA AND LATARGET. 1947. *J. Bact., 53,* 149.

MAZIA. 1949. Personal Communication.

MITCHELL. 1942. *Brit. J. Exp. Path., 23,* 296.

PANIGÈLE. 1948. Personal Communication.

SANGER. 1945. *Biochem. J., 39,* 507.

STEDMAN AND STEDMAN. 1943. *Nature, 152,* 556.

THORELL. 1947. *Cold Spring Harbor Symposia, 12.*

CHAPTER 6

QUANTITATIVE STUDIES
IN CYTOCHEMISTRY

My own contribution to quantitative studies in cytochemistry has been limited to pointing out some of the theoretical difficulties in this field. The requirements of a system which will permit quantitative studies are far from generally appreciated, and the purpose of this chapter is to set out briefly the more general requirements, so that the limitations of individual studies may be more readily assessed. Since it is not practicable to give a detailed account of all possible requirements in all possible situations, I shall limit the discussion to rather general problems, and it should not be supposed that a study which complies with the points to be set out is necessarily adequate. On the other hand, any study which does not provide adequately for the solution of all the problems which will be set out here is certainly inadequate. The problems which will be considered are the following:

1. Errors due to scattering and refraction.
2. Adherence to the Beer-Lambert law.
3. Errors due to states of aggregation.
4. Errors due to fixation and diffusion.
5. Errors due to inadequate chemical procedures.
6. Damage caused to specimen by illumination.

Errors Due to Scattering and Refraction

In almost all quantitative cytochemical studies, the experimental procedure is to estimate the proportion of light which is transmitted by the specimen at a variety of wavelengths. Since cells are too small to permit such studies without magnification, the experimental procedure involves examination of the distribution of light in a microscope image of the object, by means of either a photographic method or some form of photocell. The distribution of light in the image may be influenced by the

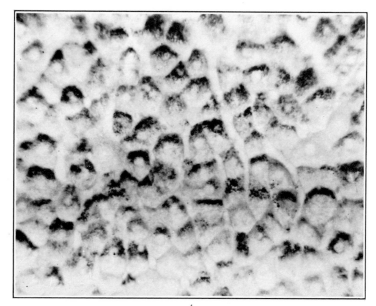

A

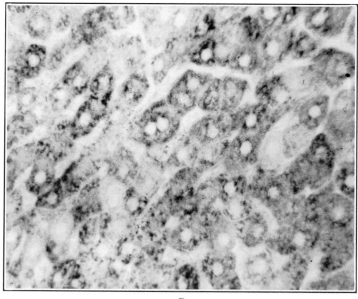

B

PLATE I. Comparison of freeze-drying and chemical fixation. Both figures show glycogen in rat liver as demonstrated by the reaction with periodate (see Chapter 4). Figure A shows the effect of fixing with 80 percent alcohol. Figure B is a frozen-dried preparation. Figure A shows a polarised distribution of glycogen, as though the cells had been centrifuged. Figure B shows the physiological condition of the tissue. Preparations by L. G. Bell.

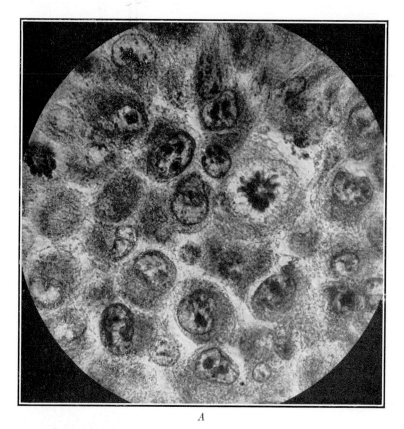

A

PLATE II. Comparison of freeze-drying and chemical fixation. Both figures
are ultraviolet photographs of Walker rat sarcoma, taken by R. King;
2570 A.U.; 2-mm. quartz objective. Figure A shows fixation by Carnoy's
method, and Fig. B by freeze-drying. Note that with chemical fixation
there is a halo surrounding the metaphase plate, and the intermitotic nuclei

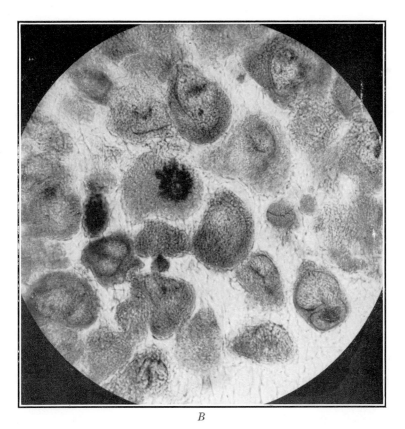

B

show much contrast, whereas with freeze-drying the cytoplasm absorbs ultraviolet light more or less uniformly right up to the metaphase plate, and there is comparatively little contrast in the intermitotic nuclei. Figure *B* resembles ultraviolet photographs of undamaged living cells, and Fig. *A* resembles ultraviolet photographs of damaged cells.

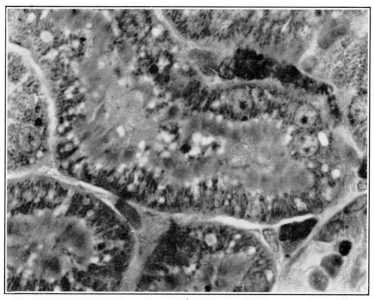

A

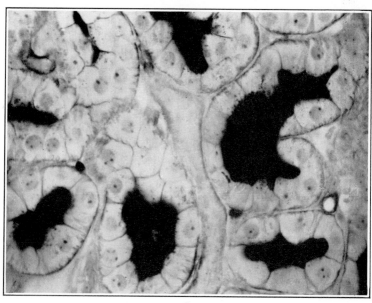

B

PLATE III. Two examples of rat-kidney sections prepared by the freeze-drying method, and then treated by cytochemical techniques. Figure *A* shows a section treated by the tetrazodianisidine technique, followed by K acid (see Chapter 5). Note the excellent preservation of the mitochondria and the nuclei, and the fine detail of the free borders of the secretory cells demonstrated in the central tubule (L. G. Bell). Figure *B* shows a similar section treated by the glycerophosphate technique for alkaline phosphatase; incubation time, 20 minutes. All the structures in Fig. *B* appear by virtue of their phosphatase content only. Note that phosphatase, though most abundant in the secretory borders of tubule cells, is evident also in all cell borders of the tubule cells. Note also the uniform distribution of phosphatase in the nuclei apart from the nucleoli, which are richer in phosphatase than the remainder of the nucleus.

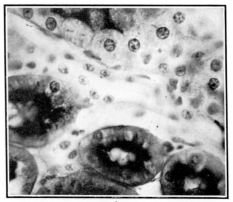

A

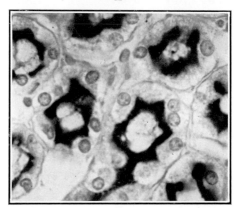

B

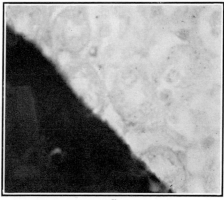

C

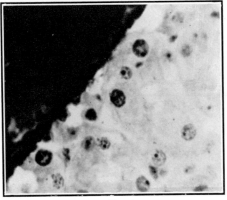

D

PLATE IV. Rat-kidney tubule sections (fixative 80 percent alcohol), demonstrating the Gomori-Takamatsu technique for alkaline phosphatase. Figure *A*, incubated 20 minutes. Compare this figure with Plate III, Fig. *B*. By comparison the nuclei of the alcohol-fixed section are grossly precipitated, and during fixation phosphatase has diffused from the cell borders into the cytoplasm. Figure *B*, incubated 5 minutes: the main sites of phosphatase are already apparent. Figure *C* is a section containing phosphatase superimposed on a section in which phosphatase has been destroyed. Incubation time, 320 minutes. The active section has been grossly overincubated and appears almost opaque. The microscope was focussed on the underlying section, which is devoid of phosphatase activity, but which shows a faint image by diffraction. The absence of any apparent phosphatase activity in the underlying section shows that, during the incubation period of 320 minutes, no significant amount of phosphatase or of calcium phosphate has diffused into the underlying section, so that there is clearly no significant diffusion artefact. Figure *D* is the same as Fig. *C*, but incubated 640 minutes. By this time some of the nuclei of the underlying inert section appear black, showing that either calcium phosphate or phosphatase has diffused into the underlying section. The intensity of staining of the nuclei of the inert section has been deliberately exaggerated in the photograph to provide contrast with the unstained background seen by diffraction.

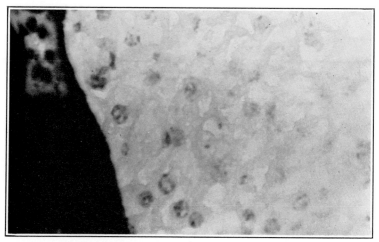

A

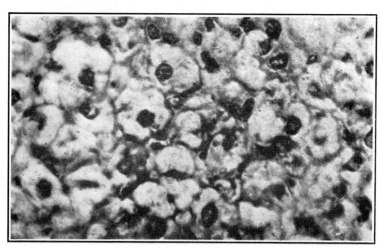

B

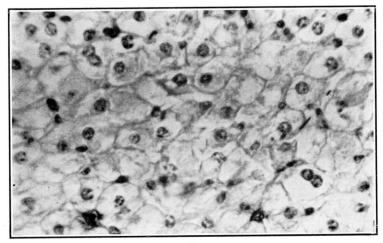

C

Plate V. Experiments on the diffusion of phosphatase during use of the Gomori-Takamatsu technique. Figure A, guinea-pig kidney superimposed on inert section of guinea-pig liver, incubated 1280 minutes. Note that the staining artefact on the inert section extends seven or more cell diameters from the opaque active section. Figure B, photograph of liver section. This was an inert section, upon which an active kidney section was superimposed, in buffer, for 2 days. Then the active section was removed, and the previously inert section incubated for 1280 minutes, with the result shown in the figure. All the blackening shown represents phosphatase activity. Since the active section was removed prior to incubation, the factor which had diffused from the active to the inert section must be either phosphatase or phosphatase activator. Figure C, intrinsic phosphatase of guinea-pig liver: incubation time 1280 minutes. The phosphatase intrinsic to the liver sections of Figs. A and B was destroyed. Comparison of the three figures shows that the artefact phosphatase has a different distribution from the intrinsic phosphatase.

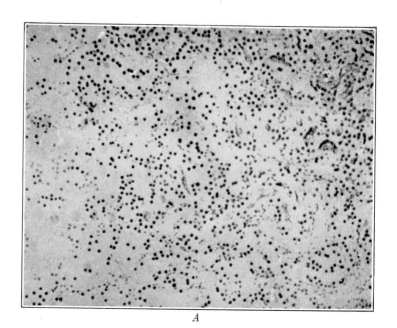

A

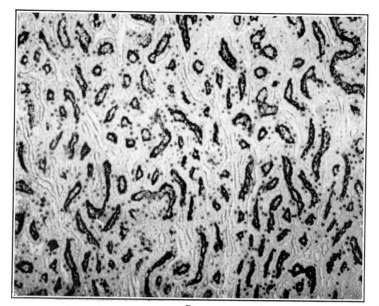

B

PLATE VI. Rat-kidney phosphatase by the method of Loveless and Danielli. Figure *A* shows a section incubated with substrate and *p*-nitrophenylazo-4-naphthol. This mixture contains no activator for brush-border phosphatase, so that only nuclear phosphatase is demonstrated. Figure *B*, same as Fig. *A*, but incubation carried out with activators for both brush-border and nuclear phosphatases.

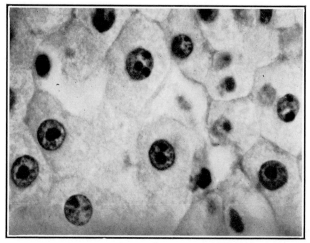

A

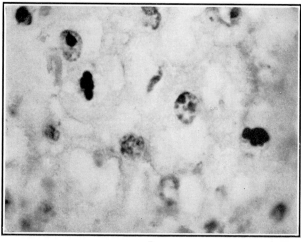

B

PLATE VII. Figure *A*, phosphatase of normal rat liver: note high concentration in nucleoli. Figure *B*, phosphatase of regenerating liver: note nuclear phosphatase concentrated on chromosomes (shown as equatorial plate). Figure *C*, Feulgen of Walker rat sarcoma: fixative Carnoy. Figure

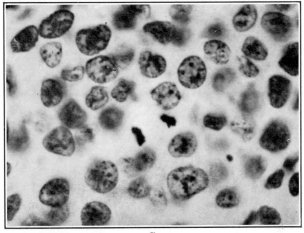

C

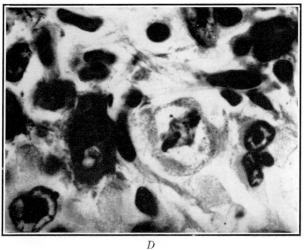

D

D, phosphatase of Walker rat sarcoma: note high concentration of phosphatase in nucleoli, mitotic chromosomes, and also on spindle. Fixative for phosphatase preparations, 80 percent alcohol; incubation time, 120 minutes.

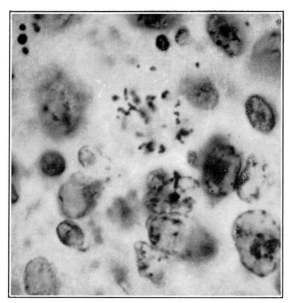

A

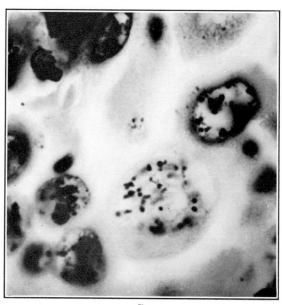

B

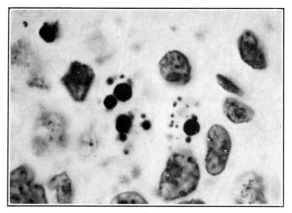

C

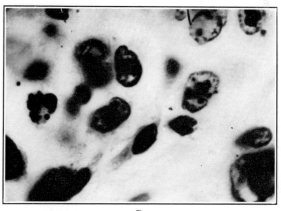

D

PLATE VIII. Walker rat sarcoma 4 days after treatment by nitrogen mustard. Figures *A* and *C*, Feulgen; fixative, Carnoy. Figures *B* and *D*, alkaline phosphatase by Gomori-Takamatsu method; fixative, 80 percent alcohol; incubation time, 120 minutes. Note parallelism between distribution of phosphatase and deoxy nucleic acid. Figures *A* and *B* show cells in which spindle formation has failed, so that metaphase chromosomes are scattered throughout the cytoplasm. Figures *B* and *D* show pycnotic degeneration.

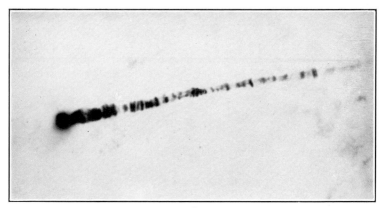

A

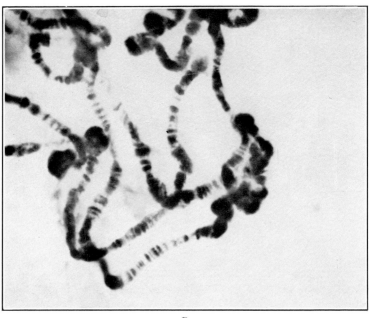

B

PLATE IX. Alkaline phosphatase of *Drosophila* salivary chromosomes by Gomori-Takamatsu method. Fixative, 3.8 percent acetic acid, followed by 95 percent alcohol; incubation time, 1280 minutes.

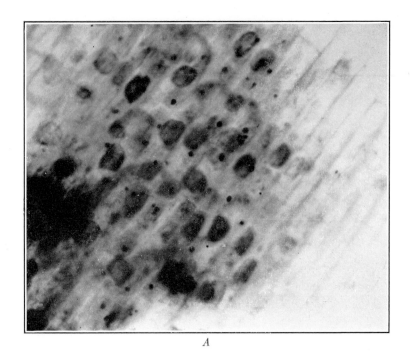

A

PLATE X. Alkaline phosphatase of onion root tips. Fixative, 80 percent alcohol. Figure *A*, with glycerophosphate as substrate.

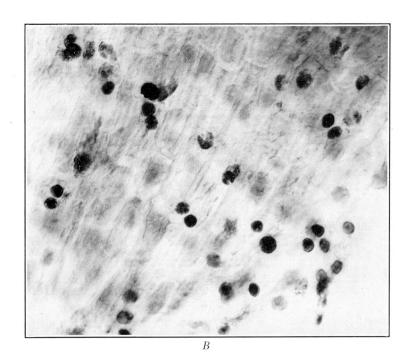

B

PLATE X. Alkaline phosphatase of onion root tips. Fixative, 80 percent alcohol. Figure B, with β-naphtholphosphate as substrate.

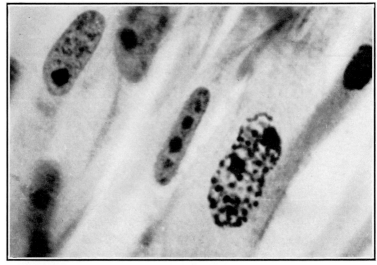

A

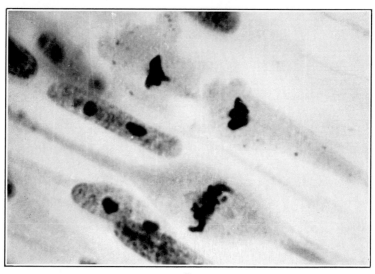

B

PLATE XI. Alkaline phosphatase of chick osteoblast cultures. Cultures by H. B. Fell. Fixative 80 percent alcohol; incubation time, 1280 minutes; substrate, glycerophosphate. Figure *A*, prophase and intermitotic nuclei: note high phosphatase concentration in nucleoli, still visible in prophase,

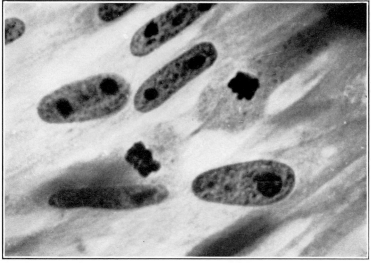

C

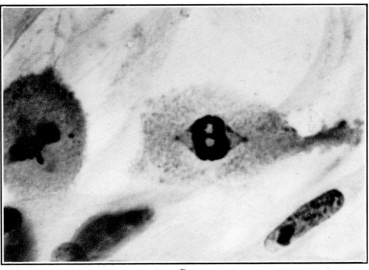

D

and high concentration on prophase chromosomes. Figure *B*, note metaphase plate and anaphase. Figure *C*, note anaphase. Figure *D*, note metaphase plates. There appears to be phosphatase on the spindles and centrosomes.

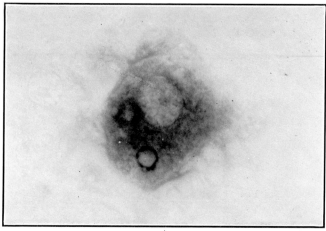

A

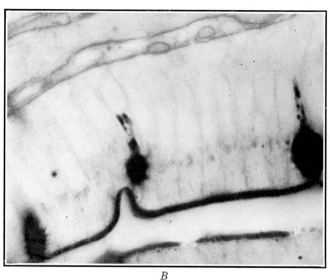

B

PLATE XII. Figure *A*, aldehyde in a single liver cell. The large, clear spherical body is the nucleus, and the two dark rings are zones of high aldehyde content surrounding two fat droplets. There is also diffuse aldehyde in the cytoplasm. The surrounding cells are devoid of aldehyde. Figure *B*, carbohydrate in rat intestinal mucosa, revealed by periodate oxidation. Note high concentrations in the absorbing borders and in the goblet cells, and a much lower concentration in the Golgi zone of the absorbing cells.

scattering and refraction of light in the object, as well as by the absorption of photons by individual constituents of the object. Since the analysis of the distribution of chemical substances in the specimen depends entirely on the amount of absorption of light, it is necessary to reduce the effects of scattering and refraction to a minimum, and, if these effects are still significant, to make measurements of the errors due to them in order to correct apparent absorption values. Caspersson has set out these problems in some detail. His chief conclusions are as follows:

1. The object must be clearly resolved. A satisfactory absorption curve cannot be obtained if the diameter of the object is less than three times the wavelength of the light used.

2. It is not sufficient to measure the absorption of light at one wavelength only, because the absorption bands of the various components of tissues overlap to a considerable degree.

3. The optical system must fulfill Abbe's sine condition. Otherwise the distribution of light in the image does not correspond to that in the object.

4. Every point in the object must be illuminated by incoherent light, as, for example, by using Köhler's method of illumination.

5. A correction must be applied for the amount of light lost by scattering. This is best done by measuring the amount of light actually scattered. A much more common procedure is to measure the loss of light in the specimen at a wavelength at which the specimen is believed to have practically no power of absorbing light. The light loss at this wavelength is then assumed to be caused by scattering. It is then commonly assumed that the scattering is varying inversely as the fourth power of the wavelength, and the light loss by scattering at other wavelengths is calculated on this basis. This method is by no means satisfactory, since, whereas the loss of light varies as $1/\lambda^n$, where λ is the wavelength, the value of n is a function of particle size in the specimen and varies from 2 to 4 for particles between 10 $m\mu$ and 10 μ in diameter. Since this is a range of particle sizes to be expected in cells, the correction is obviously difficult to make from observations at one wavelength. From this point of view there is much to be said for working at as large a wavelength as is compatible with adequate resolving power.

6. To minimise scattering and refraction, the specimen must be mounted in a medium of as nearly as possible the same refractive index as the specimen. Caspersson suggests that the ratio of the two refractive indexes should not exceed 1.1.

7. If the points mentioned above are adequately taken into consideration, including the limit to the ratio of the refractive indexes of specimen and mounting medium, then Caspersson calculates that the minimum permissible numerical aperture which can be used is 0.85.

Adherence to the Beer-Lambert Law

When an adequate optical system has been used, and losses of light by scattering and refraction minimised, the difference of the intensities of the light incident upon the specimen and that transmitted is due to absorption of photons. The question then arises: what is the relationship between the amount of light absorbed and the number of absorbing molecules. It is commonly assumed that this relationship is given by the Beer-Lambert law, i.e.:

$$E = \log I_0/I = ecd$$

where E = extinction, I_0 = intensity of light entering specimen, I = intensity of light leaving specimen, e = extinction coefficient, c = concentration of absorbing substance, and d = thickness of absorbing layer. This postulated linearity between the extinction and concentration is by no means an unbreakable rule, and, unfortunately, in biological systems, as Caspersson has noted, it is difficult to obtain adequate evidence of the extent to which the rule is valid. The conditions prevailing in fixed specimens are difficult to evaluate from the point of view of the relationship between E and c. Errors due to fluorescence may also be of importance: these can be detected by use of a fluorescence microscope.

Commoner has made valuable contributions to this field. In an elegant paper he showed that the Beer-Lambert law was valid for the pigments in *Coleus* hair cells. And in an interesting paper written with Lipkin he pointed out that, where the specimen under examination contains optically anisotropic molecules, marked deviations from the Beer-Lambert law occur if the anisotropic molecules are markedly oriented. In the case of an army of molecules which are completely oriented, with unpolarised light the extinction is proportional to the number of molecules only at relatively low extinction values (less than 0.15). As the concentration rises E deviates increasingly from the linear relationship, and as E approaches 0.3 the extinction becomes independent of the number of absorbing molecules: the proportion of light absorbed may never exceed 50 percent. With such a system, containing oriented anisotropic molecules, it is possible to obtain reliable results only if the specimen is examined with polarised light.

Although it is probable that serious errors due to orientation of anisotropic molecules are rare, the danger of error is none the less very real. It has been shown by Schmidt (1937), Frey-Wyssling (1948), Caspersson (1950), and others that nucleic acid molecules are markedly anisotropic and quite commonly oriented.

Errors due to States of Aggregation

These may be classified into two groups: errors due to the aggregation of individual molecules, and errors due to aggregates of size near the limit of resolution.

Even when the group which is absorbing light is known, it is not always easy to define its absorption band in a specimen. The position of an absorption band may often be readily altered by the formation of complexes with other substances in the specimen. Well-known examples of this are the change in colour of astaxanthin from red to blue when it is adsorbed on certain proteins, and the wide variations in the spectrum of haem when it is adsorbed upon different proteins. These changes in spectrum are not restricted to the visible spectrum. Caspersson has found a marked difference in the ultraviolet between the positions of the maximum of absorption by pure nucleic acid and the maximum found with nucleic acid in cells. These effects must be expected whether the absorbing molecule is an intrinsic part of the cell or an added dye; they are likely to be affected by the mode of fixation.

The second effect may be most clearly appreciated if we consider a chequerboard, as in Fig. 8. The square as a whole is the area whose absorption is under consideration. The hatched areas contain a high concentration of absorbing substance; the clear areas have no absorbing material. Consider the case in which the concentration of absorbing material in the hatched areas is so high that, if a large area had the same composition as the hatched areas, practically no light would be transmitted. Then the actual absorption of light by a chequered area depends upon the relationship between the distance d and the wavelength of light.

If $d \gg \lambda$, the chequers will be clearly resolved and the area will transmit 50 percent of the incident light. If $\lambda \gg d$, the chequers will not be resolved, and the transmission of light will be practically nil. If d is of the order of $\lambda/3$ or $\lambda/4$, the percentage of transmission is unpredictable. The great danger therefore lies in this region, since the chequers cannot be resolved when d is of this order of $\lambda/3$ or $\lambda/4$. Thus, in a specimen in which the absorbing material is aggregated in this way, errors of hundreds of

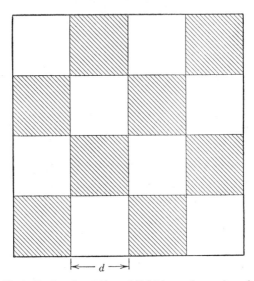

Fig. 8. To illustrate the absorption of light by a chequerboard distribution of an absorbing substance. The areas containing the absorbing substance will be resolvable if $d > \lambda/2$.

percent could arise in calculating the concentration of absorbing substances from extinctions.

Probably the most effective way of surmounting this latter difficulty is to study a specimen at several different regions of the spectrum.

ERRORS DUE TO FIXATION AND DIFFUSION

Displacement of substances in the cell by diffusion may occur at the time of fixation or at a later stage of treatment. As was indicated in Chapter 2, the only reliable method of fixation for tissues is freeze-drying. Diffusion, however, may occur even within the medium used for mounting a section, or during the various stages of a cytochemical reaction. A method of study which has general validity for the detection of diffusion arte-facts is to use superimposed sections, with the section to be studied superimposed upon a similar section which is devoid of the substance under investigation. This technique has been discussed previously in this volume, and in two earlier papers (Danielli, 1946, 1949). So far, however, no studies have been made of diffusion during paraffin infiltration and embedding. Although diffusion in paraffin is unlikely to be significant when such substances as nucleic acid are considered, with many of the substances for which the microincineration technique has been used the errors may be serious.

It should be feasible to study diffusion in wax, by means of the superimposed-section technique.

As a result of fixation marked increases usually occur in the refractive-index differences between different parts of cells, and as a result diffraction and light scattering become more pronounced. Caspersson suggests that this may be minimised by either of two methods. The first is that commonly practiced in microscopic work—namely, mounting the specimen in a medium of the same refractive index as the part of the specimen to be examined. A second most ingenious device, probably applicable only to frozen-dried material, is to make use of the very slow diffusion of proteins, etc., which occurs in specimens mounted in glycerol. When a frozen-dried specimen is mounted in glycerol the boundaries of the various cell organs are sharp, and the resultant abrupt discontinuities in refractive index cause marked losses of light. But after some time in glycerol a small degree of diffusion reduces the sharpness of the boundaries, so that there are continuous rather than discontinuous changes in refractive index, and light losses are correspondingly reduced.

Errors due to Inadequate Chemical Procedures

The first requirements of a cytochemical reaction are that the end-products should be known and either non-diffusible or readily examined by techniques for detecting diffusion. Attention has already been directed to these problems in preceding parts of this book. For quantitative studies a further chemical problem becomes prominent, for it is necessary to know to what extent the cytochemical reaction is quantitative. The requisite information is seldom available at the present time.

This latter problem is by no means simple. Suppose, for example, that we consider a reaction such as that of dinitrofluorobenzene with tyrosine. With free tyrosine the reaction is rapid and quantitative, but with a protein steric effects may be sufficient to mask some reactive groups from the reagent. When denaturation occurs, some masked groups may be exposed to the reagent, and other hitherto exposed groups may be masked. Thus the results obtained may be a function of the degree of denaturation. Material which has been frozen-dried is probably little denatured but, on the other hand, can rarely be used without further denaturation. And the greater the denaturation, the greater is the deviation of masked groups from that prevailing in the intact cell. Consequently, before commencing a study of proteins it is necessary to decide first whether what is wanted is a measure of the total concentration of a particular amino acid, or whether it is the concentration of these groups which is sterically unmasked in the native protein. And, when this decision has been made, it still remains to design an effective way of getting the required information.

Damage Caused by Illumination

When work is being done in the visible region of the spectrum, damage caused to the specimen by the incident illumination is unlikely to be serious, but as one moves into the ultraviolet the hazard steadily becomes greater. First, it becomes impossible to make continuous studies upon living cells, and then as the energy of the incident radiation increases damage to the specimen on the chemical level may become evident. This hazard can probably be adequately allowed for by measuring changes in extinction with time.

With studies in the electron microscope damage again may be caused by the electron beam. The magnitude of this damage on the chemical level has yet to be explored.

REFERENCES

Caspersson. 1947. *Symp. Soc. Exp. Biol.*, *1*, 127.
           1950. *Cell Growth and Cell Function* (Norton, New York).
Commoner. 1948. *Ann. Mo. Bot. Gard.*, *35*, 239.
           1949. *Science, 110*, 31.

COMMONER AND LIPKIN. 1949. *Science, 110,* 41.

DANIELLI. 1946. *Nature, 157,* **755**.

1947. *Symp. Soc. Exp. Biol., 1,* 101.

1949. *Cold Spring Harbor Symposia, 14,* 32.

FREY-WYSSLING. 1948. *Submicroscopic Morphology of Protoplasm* (Elsevier, Amsterdam).

SCHMIDT. 1937. *Die Doppelbrechung von Karyoplasma, etc.* (Berlin).

CHAPTER 7

THE FUTURE OUTLOOK
IN CYTOCHEMISTRY

Of the many fields of cytology, cytochemistry has probably been that which has grown most rapidly and been the scene of the most intense activity in the past ten years. The next ten or twenty years must inevitably see the consolidation of this field, the refinement of many methods, and the invention of many new methods. These activities seem likely to fall into three groups:

1. The study of qualitative methods.
2. The study of quantitative methods.
3. The application of cytochemistry to the study of the fundamental problems of cell biology.

Under the first of these headings we must envisage the extension of studies to other regions of the spectrum, including the far ultraviolet and the infrared, the development of new microscopic instruments, particularly reflecting microscopes and perhaps also the television microscope now being studied by A. K. Parpart. The refinement of electron-microscope methods is much to be hoped for. Methods involving the use of radioactive isotopes may become prominent. The investigation of fluorescence methods and the use of specific quenching agents can be anticipated. Great prominence will probably be given to methods for the localization of enzymes and the study of substrate specificity as a means of revealing the diversity of enzymes in cells. And the method recently published by Coons and his colleagues, of using tagged antibodies, if sufficiently sensitive may be of the greatest value in studying a wide variety of proteins.

In the study of quantitative methods probably the main tasks are the defining of the limits of accuracy which can be obtained, from both the chemical and the physical viewpoints. The development of more sensitive photocells, for example, is likely to be valuable, provided that the extent to which cytochemical reactions are quantitative is adequately explored, and that more attention is paid to losses of light by scattering, etc.

The biological problems which can be studied by cytochemical methods are already numerous, and beyond doubt the number will increase rapidly. A very profitable field to survey will be that of finding the relationship between purified enzymes and intracellular enzymes. To a considerable degree the biologist must look upon purified enzymes as artefacts, and, as indicated in the chapter on phosphatase, to proceed from knowledge of purified enzymes to knowledge of their biological function may be a long and difficult journey. It is certainly a journey which can be shortened by cytochemical studies. Valuable examinations will also be made of the extent to which the biochemical theories of metabolic pathways are valid. At present almost all the evidence on the nature of metabolic pathways has been built up by *in vitro* studies of enzyme systems and by a limited number of genetical studies. Some degree of confirmation of these theories is being obtained by the use of isotopes, but it is doubtful if isolation of isotope-tagged compounds from living tissues will finally solve many problems. The chemist who cannot think of a variety of alternative relationships between the members of a given set of tagged intermediates is unusually lacking in ingenuity. Cytochemical studies, by revealing the distribution of enzymes and substrates in the different phases of cell activity, can contribute greatly to this field.

The biochemistry of tissues is at present a very rough-and-ready affair. The histologist knows that all tissues are compounded of a wide variety of cells, all of which must be indiscriminately ground up together in the formation of "acetone-extracted powders," homogenates, breis, and microsome suspensions, etc. The cytochemist knows not only that these various cells are chemically different but also that even cells of the same type may, in different parts of an organ, be widely different. For example, the hepatic cells close to the central vein in a hepatic unit may differ widely from the more peripheral cells in their content of nucleic acid, phosphatase, fat, and glycogen, and so they may be in markedly different physico-chemical states. The combination of the present undiscriminating approach of the biochemist and the more perceptive but undeveloped approach of the cytologist should be richly rewarding.

The situation is the same in comparative biochemistry. At present comparative biochemistry is founded on the results obtained on a small number of so-called *typical* animals, plants, yeasts, and bacteria. The sole basis of the claim that these organisms are typical rests upon the facts that all of them may, by rather simple methods, be obtained in great quantities and that many of them have been prominent in the preliminary medical biology courses and their equivalents. The great majority of living organisms cannot be obtained in sufficient quantity for biochemical studies without immoderate and unjustified expense. But cytochemistry has the potentiality of throwing almost the whole of the living world open to study by the chemist.

Medicine and agriculture cannot fail to benefit from the fundamental studies just outlined, but in addition to this there is promise for the direct sudy of pathological conditions by cytochemical methods. For example, studies of gene action, of the evolution of genes and viruses, and of differentiation hold great promise for the elucidation of the nature of cancer and the development of new drugs for the treatment of cancer. It has already been shown that various tumours are particularly rich in certain enzymes. This in itself has been effective in promoting the study of new types of drugs. The drugs which are in use at present lack selectivity so that, although they have a potent action on tumour cells, their use is restricted by their high general toxicity. At King's College we are now investigating the use of drugs which are comparatively inert, but which, upon coming into contact with an enzyme present in high concentration in a tumour cell, liberate a derivative of very high activity. Thus we hope that, by designing a drug to fit the enzymic pattern of a tumour, we may attain a much higher degree of specificity of drug action.

Equally, we can expect assistance in diagnosis. A biopsy specimen can seldom provide sufficient material for a variety of biochemical tests, but it is sufficient for dozens of cytochemical tests.

Thus the outlook in cytochemistry is full of promise. This promise, however, will only be fulfilled if cytochemistry is used as a rigorous technique by an adequately trained staff.

REFERENCE

COONS. 1952. *Symp. Soc. Exp. Biol., 6* (in press).

INDEX

(For author references, *see* pages 15, 27, 77, 94, 124, 132, 136)